Praise for *The Frosell Affair*

"Buried among the tales of heroism that arose from WWII are stories that demonstrate the hideous lengths to which 'heroes' will go to reclaim a nation's greatness and wealth. *The Frosell Affair* is just such a story, that has the misfortune of being true. Written by the youngest member of the Frosell family, it illustrates, perhaps more than anything, the fine, hazy line between perseverance and obsession."

—Maya Kaathryn Bohnhoff, *New York Times* best-selling author of
The Antiquities Hunter

"Historical nonfiction at its finest—a rich philanthropist, a devious international plot to steal his wealth, and his seemingly endless, harrowing fight to clear his name and reclaim his fortune. Splashed across the backdrop of Charles de Gaulle's France, peopled with Nazis, corrupt diplomats, and villains of all stripes, *The Frosell Affair* is a serious page-turner."

—David Niall Wilson, *USA Today* best-selling author of
The Orffyreus Wheel and *Nevermore: A Novel of Love, Loss, &
Edgar Allan Poe*

"Heddy Frosell da Ponte has re-created post-war France so well here one can feel the distant thud of the shells of the Allied invasion and the fearsome crackle of machine gun fire on the streets of Paris as Nazi collaborators are rounded up and dealt swift justice by de Gaulle's underground resistance. In this true story of her family's struggle against the greed of the French and weakness of the Swedes (Oscar Frosell's native country), Heddy takes us on an emotional roller coaster as the authorities imprison her father on the most ludicrous, trumped-up charges while allowing the theft of all of his vast array of valuable possessions and money. While *The Frosell Affair* illustrates the ultimate betrayal of trust, it is also a story of stoicism (Oscar's wife was as equally tenacious as her husband; his lawyer the one person he was able to trust; and his little girl, Heddy, a bright, imaginative child who always made the best of her difficult life) and the unerring fight for justice against all odds. If ever a book deserved to be made into a movie, it's *The Frosell Affair*! A definite five stars from me."

—Pat Moffett, author of *Ice Cream in the Cupboard: A True Story of Early Onset Alzheimer's* (now a major motion picture) and *Fortunate Soldier*

"Alan Furst himself could not have penned a more suspenseful, gut-wrenching ode to World War II Paris. The subterfuge, duplicity, and outright greed displayed by both the French and the Swedes as they conspired to destroy the Frosell family and loot their Paris home of all its jewelry, antiques, priceless stamp collections, and money would honestly be quite unbelievable—were it not for the fact that this is a true story. Far from being a litany of facts and dates, *The Frosell Affair* (written by the protagonist's daughter, based upon her father's writings) is an electrifying thriller that has the reader rooting for the very complex Oscar Frosell, a man of heroic determination and sometimes harrowingly naive narrow perspective, a man who believes in justice even if it comes at the expense of his family. With all the threats to his life (and his wife and young daughter's), false imprisonment, living in hiding like paupers, and the ruination of a little girl's childhood, most people would have given up and returned to their home country—but not Oscar. A must-read for anyone who loves WW2 thrillers and biographies."

—James H. Longmore, author of the psychological thrillers *Flanagan, Tenebrion,* and *Pede*

"In the *New York Times* best-selling novel *The Nightingale*, Kristin Hannah tackles the often-overlooked subject of women in WW2, and in *The Frosell Affair*, Heddy Frosell da Ponte examines so-called 'heroic' men whose megalomania inflict untold trauma on the lives of the many innocent. Backed with irrefutable proof, the biography implicates President Charles de Gaulle in a conspiracy to defraud one such family, that of a wealthy Swedish businessman, Oscar Frosell, of everything he owned (inherited family wealth and business assets). But far more heartbreaking than the years-long court cases, false imprisonment, violence, and hardships, is the theft of a little girl's childhood—and the imposition of emotional burdens she would carry throughout her life. Frosell's daughter (the author) endured years without her father—even when he was not incarcerated, his every waking moment taken up by his obsession to gain restitution for his family. And while many adults reading this book will comprehend why he was so relentless, so zealous in his pursuit of what was rightfully his and his family's, it's not so easy for a small child to puzzle out, especially when all she's wanting is for Daddy to take her to the zoo. Rest assured, *The Frosell Affair* is quite a story—very much recommended."

— Anneliese Khalil, author of *Ascension*

"The smells and textures of post-WWII Paris leap from the pages of Heddy Frosell da Ponte's true-crime thriller *The Frosell Affair.* In the aftershocks of the war, France is licking its wounds, Nazis are being gathered and dealt with, and the rule of order once again dominates Parisian streets. But da Ponte's father, Swedish business magnate and philanthropist Oscar Frosell, only escaped the occupation to find himself ensnared in a grizzly homeland plot to relieve him and his family of their vast wealth. Frosell's fortune was so great that Charles de Gaulle himself was willing to help facilitate the man's undoing to get in on the booty. From high in the ranks of the French Navy, a plan was formulated to destroy Frosell and steal his fortune by any means necessary. To that end, the man was falsely imprisoned, ignored by the Swedish Consulate (which chose to work in lockstep with the French government), and spuriously debased as a criminal and Nazi sympathizer. Frosell fought for years to clear his name and protect his fortune, which consisted not only of money but of priceless jewels, antiquities, art collections, and more. Unfortunately, while attempting to right the injustices and take back what was rightfully his, he also put his family through hell. That's the true-life tale deftly laid out in this nail-biter, but not what the book is really about. *The Frosell Affair* owned me from the beginning as we hear about this man's obsessions and dangerous endeavors through the eyes of his young daughter, the author. While her father fought to save his treasures, he stole his daughter's childhood; in trying to destroy his enemies, he robbed her of his affection, attention, and compassion. As the adage asks—'What price glory?' This is a must-read for fans of high-voltage true-crime thick with political intrigue—and for folks who understand too well the lifelong pursuit of a parent's love."

—Lee Adams, author of *5th and Vanguard* and *Nighthawks*
(Julie Page Mystery Series)

Frosell da Ponte (*The Glamour Years of Flying as a Stewardess*) serves up an intriguing "dramatization of the true story" of her family's experience after the 1944 Allied victory in Europe, drawn from her father's unpublished writings. In her third-person telling, her father, Oscar Frosell, an affluent Swedish national living in France, is labeled a Nazi collaborator by corrupt members of the Resistance, who are after his fortune, when the Allies liberate Paris. After he is stripped of his home, tortured, and imprisoned, Oscar enters a lengthy legal battle with the French Republic, and his quest for justice puts him at odds with some of the most lauded figures in history. Meanwhile, his obsession with restitution isolates and forever alters his daughter Heddy. The story is at its most successful when exploring Heddy's loss of innocence as she comes of age during a period of intense turmoil. She is precocious and observant, and glimpsing a father's predicament through the eyes of a child is noteworthy. While the dehumanizing treatment Oscar faces will deeply affect readers, the pursuit of wealth-based reparations can feel cold in the context of such widespread suffering. This bold narrative is remarkably different from typical novels and novelizations of World War II. The bureaucratic villains are respected real-life political figures (Charles de Gaulle,

Raoul Nordling), and, rather than focusing on the cruelty of the Nazis, the horrors of the Holocaust, or the war itself, Frosell da Ponte explores how greed and self-preservation can corrupt anyone. Though the historical accuracy of the story is largely unknown (the records of this affair are not readily available), this provocative work illuminates an atypical battle against oppression and intimidation. **Takeaway:** This challenging, original historical dramatization is perfect for those interested in moral grey areas and corrupt bureaucracy. Great for fans of: Amor Towles's *A Gentleman in Moscow*, John le Carré's *The Spy Who Came in From the Cold*.

—Publishers Weekly (BookLife Review)

THE
FROSELL
AFFAIR

HEDDY FROSELL DA PONTE

Frosell da Ponte Publishing

The following is a dramatization of the true story. Names, dates, facts, and figures are accurate, although some characters have been homogenized for clarity.

Contents

PROLOGUE

Oermigen Concentration Camp. April 18th, 1948.

The metallic clanking of steel doors and the all-too-familiar clumping of heavy footsteps awoke Oscar Frosell from his fitful sleep; sound sleep was a welcome respite from the fevered nightmares that had plagued him since his incarceration at Oermigen. The bleak concentration camp had such a sinister reputation that Frosell's dreams were constantly haunted by the sad, weeping faces of Marie, his darling wife, and Heddy, his beautiful little girl—faces he feared deep in his soul he was unlikely to see again.

The footsteps grew ever closer, resounding ominously about the dark, dank stone walls of the prison and accompanied by the disjointed chatter of deep French voices and bursts of raucous laughter.

Frosell had never craved a cigarette quite as much as he did right then. He had been denied the privilege since his arrival at Oermigen, almost two weeks ago, and he wanted nothing more than to feel the comforting tang of scorching smoke as it rushed into his lungs, accompanied by the wonderful dizzying sensation as the nicotine hit home. But, in a place where even the most basic of necessities

1

were in scant supply and prisoners were confined six to a cell for twenty-three hours a day in cold, stinking rooms originally designed for two, cigarettes were indeed a luxury. Frosell had learned early on in his ordeal that collaborators were deemed the lowest of the low—even if only alleged—both at Oermigen and in each one of the prisons he had been forced to endure over the past three years. To the French, collaborators were lower in some eyes than even the Germans they were accused of colluding with, whether they were guilty or not.

Frosell shivered beneath the scratchy, threadbare blanket, the clammy chill of prison air clinging to his bones. His back throbbed out its own protest against the lumpy, straw-filled mattress, which was a world apart from the luxurious bed and sumptuous Egyptian cotton sheets he'd shared with Marie at their Rue Dufrenoy apartment, what felt to be a lifetime ago. Thoughts of Marie and Heddy spun around in his mind once more, their faces alight with joy and laughter in happier times. Frosell was a man blessed with an iron will and strong constitution, but while he was no longer afraid of what fate awaited him, his fears lay with his wife and daughter—what would become of them once he was no longer there as their protector?

The guards' footsteps came to a sudden halt, and their booming voices echoed about the darkness beyond the cell walls. Frosell prayed silently to a God he felt in his heart had forsaken him.

The door burst open. A vicious flash of torchlight pierced the pitch black of Frosell's cell, stabbing at his eyes.

Then, hands were upon him. Powerful fingers dug hard into the flesh of his upper arms as Frosell was dragged from the cruel comfort of the foul mattress and out into the chill air beyond the cell.

The guards wore the regulation ill-fitting dark blue uniforms that appeared an ominous black in the yellow light of the prison walkway. Unshaven and stinking of cheap cigarettes and even cheaper booze, the guards, Frosell assumed, were most likely angry at having been seconded to the night shift; dragging prisoners from their cells in the small hours was a common occurrence at Oermigen. It was little more than sport for the guards, something to break up the monotony of long, cold nights patrolling the hallways of the prison, serenaded by the mournful weeping of their charges.

"*Sous-merde!*" a venomous voice boomed in Frosell's ear as he tried desperately to gain his footing against the slick stone of the prison hallway; the skin was already scraped from the tops of his bare feet and toes.

"*Collaborateur,*" hissed the second voice, and Frosell felt the warm dampness of the guard's spit as it splashed his cheek.

Frosell knew there was little point arguing. He was in Oermigen because he'd been found guilty of the most heinous crime of collaboration, and the pair of rough, burly guards couldn't have cared less to hear his protestations of innocence, trumped-up charges, betrayal by his own countrymen, and de Gaulle's complicity in his circumstance.

Frosell found his feet as the guards hurried him along toward an arched wooden door set among the moss-stained bricks at the end of the hallway. His legs, weakened by so much inactivity, struggled to keep up the brisk pace as he was nearly dragged through the darkness.

In his days in the French Foreign Legion, Frosell would have easily overpowered the pair of them. He could have snapped their scrawny, impudent necks like kindling twigs, but the years of incarceration had left his body weakened—although his resolve remained unwavering. One of the guards kicked at the door with a heavy boot. It crashed open to reveal a small courtyard lit by a trio of flickering gaslights and the white sparkling stars in the night sky.

Frosell's heart pounded hard and heavy in his chest, his tongue dry and stuck to the roof of his desiccated mouth as his worst fears gripped him. This was one part of Oermigen he had yet to visit, but he'd overheard other prisoners speak of it in hushed, terrified voices; many accused collaborators had paid this tiny, moss-lined courtyard a visit, and not one of them had returned. People simply disappeared here, the word *oubliettes* thrown around like it was almost something pleasant, even though its translation was "never seen again."

The guards dragged Frosell into the courtyard and slammed the door shut behind them; the heavy wood creaked its loud complaint as it crashed home against the warped frame. With rough hands and drunken grunts of exertion, the guards shoved him up against the moist, dark-stained wall at the far end—so hard the wind was knocked from his lungs.

"Die like a coward, collaborator!" the taller of the guards snarled at Frosell. He dangled a filthy, bloodstained blindfold in front of his prisoner's face, clearly expecting Frosell to break down, weep, and beg for his life.

But Oscar Frosell was made of stronger stuff than that. He stood proud against the dank wall and remained determined to not give the sadistic guards the satisfaction of showing any weakness, even though his heart cried out for his wife and daughter. He shrugged off the blindfold and fixed the guard with a steely glare, determined to remain defiant to the very end.

The guard shrugged and placed a broad, meaty hand on Frosell's chest to push him tight against the chill dampness of the courtyard wall. The still-fresh blood splashed upon the brick soaked through Frosell's thin, cotton prison-issued shirt and onto his shivering skin.

The second guard, with a sick grin splitting his bristly face, un-holstered his Luger and pressed it hard against Frosell's temple; the icy metal of the gun's muzzle indented the accused man's pale, sun-starved skin.

Frosell stared the man directly in the eyes, his mind swirling with comforting thoughts of the dear, sweet faces of Marie and Heddy. His heart was saddened beyond comprehension that he would never get to hold them in his arms again, and that his ignominious end was to destroy his family once and for all.

"Any last words, *collaborateur*?" the guard snarled, his breath sour and stinking.

Oscar Frosell chose to say nothing. Instead, he searched the myriad stars that twinkled and shone high above the miserable courtyard.

"Have it your way, *connard*," the guard growled as the courtyard echoed with the sound of his gun cocking.

CHAPTER ONE

6 Rue Dufrenoy, Paris, France. June 1944.

"You have such a beautiful home, Mary!" Charlotte Ducasse gushed, her mind awhirl at the sheer opulence of the Frosells' apartment. "You didn't tell me it was this grand, Madame Dumesnil!"

The admiral's wife, a tall, proud Russian lady, clasped her friend's hand in hers and smiled sweetly. "Just wait until you see the rest of the place," she said. "There are *twenty-five* rooms in all, isn't that right, Marie?"

Mme Ducasse looked mortified. "I am *so* sorry," she gasped. "I've been calling you Mary all evening."

"Everyone does." Madame Dumesnil placed a comforting hand on her friend's arm. "Even though her name *is* actually Marie."

Marie Frosell nodded, a wry smile on her full, crimson lips; Madame Dumesnil had a strange habit of late of showing off the Frosells' home as if it were her own, living vicariously by the opulence Oscar's family had built up there. It amused Marie to no end, having the wife of such a respected admiral of the fleet bragging on her behalf. How the woman just *loved* giving her guided tours at the Frosells' parties!

7

The apartment was, indeed, most grand, and was befitting of a man of Oscar Frosell's business and social standing. It was inevitable, since his roots were embedded within an incredibly wealthy Swedish family and European aristocracy, and he had grown up surrounded by such opulence and accustomed to the finest things in life. Frosell's father—a citizen of Sweden—was one of the most prominent and renowned engineers of his time. He had earned his good name—and a considerable fortune along with it—by designing and building railroad stations in the mid-1800s; railways were the latest invention and newest means of transportation of the day, and so many vast fortunes were to be made within the industry. Oscar's father was also an accomplished architect who had designed King Oscar Sofiero's castle, for which he was awarded a knighthood—the *Vasa Orden*—for his services to the Swedish state and society. As for Oscar's mother, she was nothing less than a genuine Italian countess. Born Countess da Ponte, she was exceedingly rich in her own right and had amassed the multitude of exquisite antique paintings, furniture, and jewelry that Oscar inherited upon her death.

This was to be the last party before the Frosell family headed out for their annual vacation in Cosne, a much-needed relief from the stress of living in an increasingly unpredictable Paris. Oscar's soirees had been the height of the social calendar for the Paris elite since 1941, with their close neighbors Admiral and Madame Dumesnil becoming party regulars. Their daughter, Alla, even had her own apartment in the building, which had given them the perfect excuse to become firm friends with Oscar and Marie.

"It was built in 1910," Madame Dumesnil continued, much to Mme Ducasse's delight, "and one can see the Eiffel Tower from here!"

Marie rolled her eyes at this. True, the apartment building was nestled within an affluent bend of the Seine, a mere stone's throw from the Parc de Bagatelle, Arc de Triomphe, and Monsieur Eiffel's steel monstrosity, but the latter could only be viewed from the sixth floor—the very top—of the apartment building floor, and by leaning precariously from the window.

Madame Dumesnil waved over to her husband, who was deep in conversation with a handsome young air force captain they had first met over cocktails a month or two ago, when Alla had introduced the dashing Gillet Girardot as her new beau.

Alla would accompany her parents to the Frosells' parties whenever her busy schedule allowed, although she was nowhere to be seen, having abandoned her young man the minute her father began yet another retelling of his role in the Great Fire of Smyrna.

". . . and I said, he had it coming to him!" The admiral's voice carried about the room and drowned out the gentle strains of *"La fanciulla del West"* crackling from the old gramophone player.

Madame Dumesnil waved once more, this time attracting the admiral's attention. The admiral glanced across the room at his wife and duly ignored the frantic beckoning to join her, Marie, and Mme Ducasse on yet another grand tour of the Rue Dufrenoy apartment.

"He can be so stuffy at times." Madame Dumesnil laughed off her embarrassment as Mme Ducasse scrutinized her husband across the crowded room. He was wearing full naval uniform again, as he always did at Oscar's parties and when he wanted to set out to impress. But who was he out to impress tonight with his somber, dark blue regalia and twin rows of medal ribbons? Oscar and Marie had seen him often in his civilian clothes, and long gone were the days when German officers were invited to the Frosells' parties; with the ever-increasing frequency of the uprisings by the resistance against the Vichy regime and the Nazis, and talk of the imminent Allied invasion, it was best served not to be seen to be fraternizing with the occupying forces, no matter how cordial relations had seemed in the early days of the war.

Glancing across the room at his wife, Oscar Frosell was amused by the expression of quiet resignation on the face he'd fallen in love with almost eight years ago. He watched with a wry smile as Madame Dumesnil ushered Marie and the dreadful Ducasse woman off toward the bedrooms; what was it with the admiral's wife and their apartment?

"Monsieur Frosell," a voice from behind broke his reverie, "I must be going now; it is almost curfew. Thank you for inviting me."

Frosell spun around, a fine sprinkle of gray ash falling from the end of the cigarette, which protruded from an ornate holder between his thin lips. A relic from the early days of the British Raj, the cigarette holder was three inches long, made from the finest black onyx, and had a half-inch, twenty-four-karat gold band at its center; it was one of Frosell's most prized possessions, if only for the amount of use he gave it.

"Ahh, Aimee Claire!" he exclaimed, as if he had last seen his beloved secretary years ago and not a mere hour and a half. "Thank you *so much* for coming." He landed her the customary kiss on either cheek. "I hope you have enjoyed yourself."

"Very much, Monsieur Frosell," Aimee Claire lied with a wan smile. She was a middle-aged, dowdy, stern-faced, ruthlessly efficient woman. She'd attended less than a handful of her boss's gatherings in all of the five years and change she'd been in his employ. Frosell assumed Aimee Claire was of an introverted nature and didn't push the issue, since she had become an invaluable asset to his business dealings in and around Paris. In reality, Aimee Claire had never been at all comfortable around such outward shows of affluence, having been raised in more humble Catholic surroundings.

"You have a good evening," Frosell told her, "and please, do be careful out there."

"I will, Monsieur Frosell," Aimee Claire replied. She smiled her goodbyes to the half dozen or so of Frosell's guests who were eagerly awaiting his attention, and turned to go.

"Goodnight, Aimee Claire," Frosell said, and really wished she would call him Oscar.

Aimee Claire made her way out of the room, weaving between guests engrossed in deep—often too loud—conversation. The atmosphere in the room was loaded with overtones of expectation that night, with talk of the Allies, Charles de Gaulle, the routing of the German forces, and the long-hoped-for end to the war.

A small, fleeting figure surprised Aimee Claire in the extensive hallway beyond. She saw a brief flash of white cotton nightdress and heard the faint *slap-slap-slap* of tiny bare feet on the Travertine tiled floor.

"*Bonjour*, Heddy," Aimee Claire said to the seemingly empty hallway.

"Bonjour, Aimee Claire," Heddy replied from behind the King Louis hall tree, her small, round face peeping out. "Are you leaving so soon?"

Aimee Claire nodded. "I wish to be home before curfew," she explained. "And I am ready for my bed, as you should be."

Heddy stepped out from her hiding place with a sheepish grin spread across her cute little face. "I *never* get invited to any of Father's parties," she said, ever the precocious five-year-old. She gave a wistful glance toward the bustling room and all of Father's splendidly dressed guests.

Aimee Claire crouched down to Heddy's height, her arthritic knees popping like twin gunshots. "It's all boring grown-up stuff in there, Heddy. You'd be fed up and fidgeting in no time at all." She winked at the little girl. "Why do you think I'm *really* going home early?"

Heddy giggled at this, a secret shared between them. Aimee Claire had never treated Heddy like a child, and always made time to chat whenever she'd find her sitting alone in a corner with her own thoughts as Monsieur and Madame Frosell went about their ever so important business.

Aimee Claire gave Heddy a long, fond hug and bid her good night. "If I were you, I'd get myself to bed. You have an early start and a long trip tomorrow." She made her way toward the door.

"Yes, mademoiselle," Heddy replied with an impish grin. She had little intention of doing so yet but considered it most impolite to say no to an adult.

Heddy watched as the woman's distinctive plump shape disappeared behind the sliding doors of the small elevator. She hoped and prayed Aimee Claire would stay safe from the bad people with their guns and unpleasant intentions when she got outside and was swallowed up by the warm darkness of the Paris night. Satisfied her favorite member of Father's staff was definitely not returning to the apartment that night, Heddy then scampered back to her place behind the King Louis to peek in at her father's party.

The room Father set aside for entertaining—by far the biggest in their formidable home—was filled with grand-looking gentlemen in expensive suits, aside from the one wearing a full naval commander uniform, of course, and pretty ladies in elegant cocktail dresses. Everyone made the biggest effort when they were honored with an invitation to Oscar Frosell's get-togethers, the soirees being a highlight of the Parisian social calendar.

Of course, Heddy was immensely proud of her father's social standing, and a little intimidated, too. She could only begin to imagine how important he must be, judging by how everyone appeared so eager to please and bask in his company. Heddy couldn't quite make out much of what her father was talking about. It could easily have been about the time he joined the Foreign Legion during the Great War to fight on behalf of France, the adopted country he loved with such a passion. Her father had been seriously wounded during the battle in the Dardanelles and received several medals for his bravery, which made Heddy immensely proud of him. Or, he may well have been regaling his rapt guests with elaborate tales of his time spent in the elegant city of Vienna, or how he made a resounding success of the factory he built from scratch in Hamburg; it really didn't matter, for when Oscar Frosell spoke, everyone listened.

As a lover of imaginative stories, Heddy always enjoyed hearing all the tales her father told, and she already knew most of them by heart. She knew her father was born in Canada in 1894, the son of a prominent Swedish engineer and the most glamorous Italian countess, how his family were so widely traveled and lived in wonderfully exotic places as Smyrna, Greece, Turkey, and how Oscar was fortunate enough to have studied in both England and Heidelberg, Germany. It reminded Heddy of the fairy tales she read in the first-edition books Father bought for her, and many of the stories she made up for herself revolved around a handsome young businessman and his exotic Italian bride.

But, most of all, Heddy's absolute favorite story of her father's was how he came to fall so hopelessly in love with her mother. Marie was, quite simply, the love of his life, and little Heddy delighted in how her father related that story, too, without any hint of bashfulness at how smitten he'd become with the beautifully enchanting Marie. The story was simple and sweet, which made it all the more romantic.

Her father had been befriended by a brother of Marie's. The nice young man had been kind enough to invite Oscar Frosell to his home for a break, and there he had met Marie and fell instantly in love. However, everyday life had gotten in the way of true love—as it did for so many people back then—and it was many years later, in 1937, that Heddy's father returned to France to make Marie his wife.

The rest, as they say, was history.

Frosell was holding court in the center of the vast room, surrounded by priceless antiques, sumptuous rugs from far-flung, unpronounceable corners of the world, and of course, a gaggle of rapt, smartly dressed young men who hung on his every word. Back ramrod straight, head held high, Frosell commanded respect by his very presence in the room, as he bestowed wit and wisdom to all and sundry. The cigarette holder between his lips jiggled as he spoke, as if to act out each and every syllable. Heddy had rarely seen her father without a cigarette in his mouth, a thick cloud of acrid smoke swirling about his thinning hair. The only time he would refrain from his habit was when working with his beloved stamp collections. Frosell's stamp collections were the envy of the philatelic circles and were even said to rival those of England's King George VI, which were rumored to be the best in the world. The collections had been started many, many years ago by Frosell's father, who was not only an enthusiast, but had also been quick to see the investment potential of the new prepaid, self-adhesive postage system. By the time Oscar's father bequeathed them in his will, they were virtually priceless and by far, worth much more to Frosell than a quick nicotine fix.

As he spoke, Frosell would animate his words with exaggerated hand gestures, occasionally punctuating his words by stabbing at the air with the cigarette and holder he wielded as a badge of honor. Tobacco products of any nature, as with everything else in occupied Paris, were in increasingly short supply, yet he was never seen without one.

It was the same with the food and beverages Frosell insisted were served at his gatherings. In the fraught times of power cuts, gas shortages, and row upon row of empty shelves in all of Paris's food stores, Oscar Frosell always managed to find a way to provide for his guests, even if his own family went without from time to time. As the saying went, money certainly talks!

"You should be tucked up in bed, young lady." Her mother's voice startled Heddy.

Embarrassed, the little girl turned around to greet her mother with an impish grin. "Yes, Mother," Heddy replied quietly. "I was just on my way." She offered a smile at Madame Dumesnil and the lady whom she did not know, as if they would reprieve her from her bedtime sentence.

Unfortunately for Heddy, neither of the ladies said a word in her favor.

"Off you go!" Marie clapped her hands together, and the sharp noise made Heddy jump into action.

It never ceased to amaze Heddy how her mother *always* seemed to have the knack of catching her out when she least expected or wanted it—and it was usually when she was *really* up to mischief! Heddy's mind flicked back to the time, not all that long ago, when

Mother had walked in at an inopportune moment and caught her all alone in the Louis XVI salon . . .

Her impropriety had all started out quite innocently. Heddy had simply been walking by the exquisitely furnished room one boring Sunday afternoon when she'd espied the most beautiful-looking box of chocolate pralines she thought she had ever laid her eyes upon. Naturally, Heddy, being so young of age and infinitely curious, always had a problem deciding which of the sweet, delicious fillings she preferred, nor could she ever remember which ones were which, as they all looked nearly the same nestling there in the fancy box, all appearing equally mouthwatering. So, Heddy had figured out that the best way to determine which pralines were which and what fillings she liked the most within that tempting box would be to take a taste of each one—just a little one, of course!

Looking around furtively to ensure she was, indeed, all alone, Heddy had then commenced her naughty, impromptu taste test and bit off a tiny piece from the corner of each one of the chocolates in turn. The whole idea had worked out perfectly—Heddy had determined which of the treats her favorites were and which ones she would leave for her parents to eat—right up until the point her mother found her out. And, for as much as Heddy protested that it must have been Aimee Claire, Younker, the family's German shepherd, or even a sneaky mouse or two who had nibbled on the chocolates, her mother had seen right through her attempted deception. And, the worse thing of the whole sorry affair was that Mother had dealt out the most dreaded punishment of all for a young child—no dessert after dinner for five days! It was practically a life sentence for the poor little girl.

So, unwilling to incur her mother's wrath with yet further disobedience, Heddy decided the best strategy to adopt would be to simply do as she was told—no matter how exciting it was to eavesdrop on the myriad party conversations and the more often than not bad-taste and bawdy jokes; Heddy loved how grown-ups became ever more childlike the more of her father's expensive wine they consumed.

"Good night, Mother," Heddy called over her shoulder as she darted off along the hallway to her room. From out of nowhere, Younker, Heddy's constant companion and protector, appeared and padded along after the little girl; the huge, intimidating German shepherd dog had been especially trained to watch over Heddy, and, while he was gentle and protective with her, he would never allow anyone to get too close.

"Now, just wait until you see the master bedroom—you are going to just *die!*" the admiral's wife effervesced. She gripped Mme Ducasse's arm tightly and all but dragged the poor woman down the hallway.

Marie tagged along after them. As always, she was most amused by her old friend's excitement at showing off the apartment. More often, Madame Dumesnil would save the master bedroom till the very end of the tour, and certainly would never show it before the Oriental and Louis XVI salons—they had always been firm favorites with the admiral's wife. But tonight, Madame Dumesnil appeared to be overly keen to get back to the *Chateau Latour* Oscar had flowing freely back in the function room.

"Voilà!" Madame Dumesnil declared with a theatrical flourish as she flung open the ornate door to the Frosells' boudoir and clasped Mme Ducasse's hand with eager anticipation. "Oh!" she exclaimed, stopping dead in her tracks.

"Bonjour, Mama," came a husky voice from across the room.

"Alla, what are you doing in here?" Marie asked, more than a little taken aback by the presence of the statuesque raven-haired young lady standing by her dresser.

Mme Ducasse glanced nervously between the three women in the Frosells' bedroom, as if uncertain as to what ought to be said next.

"This is my daughter, Alla. And Alla, this is Mme Ducasse." Madame Dumesnil broke the awkward silence.

Alla stepped forward, placing a long string of pearls back onto Marie's dresser as she did so. There was the definite look of the guilty across her strikingly beautiful face. She held out a hand, bold and confident. "*Commandante* Dumesnil," Alla corrected her mother with a brusque firmness as she served Mme Ducasse a firm handshake. Then, turning to Marie, she offered, "I must apologize, Madame Frosell. I was looking for the bathroom and lost my way—I have drunk a little too much of your husband's fine wine, I think."

Marie eyed her friend's daughter with suspicion. She was a trifle amused to note that Alla, like her father, had come along to the party in her dark brown uniform; with de Gaulle's rise in popularity, at times the girl could be even more pretentious than the admiral.

"I'd say more than a little *too much*." Marie laughed off the uncomfortable atmosphere as she noticed several of her antique vases appeared displaced, the doors to her closet were open, and one of her mink coats was laid spread out upon the bed. "You have visited us enough to know where all six of our bathrooms are, Alla."

The commandante snorted at Marie with a look of derision in her eyes, as if in silent admonishment of the woman daring to challenge her. "It is all too easy to get turned around in your apartment, Madame Frosell," Alla said as she made her way past her mother and toward the door. Glancing about the room, taking in its gilt finery and priceless adornments, she added, "This place resembles nothing less than a small museum. Wouldn't you agree, Mme Ducasse?" Indeed, the young woman was quite correct in her assessment, as most of the Louis XVI furniture and antiques Oscar had inherited from his parents were worthy of center display in any of the world's finest museums, as was the priceless collection of sumptuous jewelry his mother had handed down to him.

Mme Ducasse managed a thin smile as Alla sauntered out of the room, leaving her mother to continue the grand guided tour of the Frosells' apartment.

Most of the guests had gone by the time Marie, Madame Dumesnil, and Charlotte Ducasse returned to the party; the threat of curfew and the risk of being shot was forever the mood killer.

Mme Ducasse wandered off to join her husband, having bid a quick goodbye to her hosts. Together, they set off to collect her coat from the cloakroom.

"Ah, there you are, my dear," Admiral Dumesnil greeted his wife as one would a long-lost friend. "I was just telling Oscar he really ought to think about getting out of Paris," he added.

"You know, you *really* should," Madame Dumesnil agreed. "The city is becoming most unsafe, especially for a small child."

"We will be just fine, thank you," Frosell assured them both. "There really is nothing for you to worry about."

The admiral puffed out his chest, a look of grave concern playing upon his rugged face. "The Allies will be on our shores any day now, Oscar. And de Gaulle's soldiers are gaining ground against the occupation almost daily," he said. He gave a cautious glance across at his daughter who looked to be deep in conversation with her gentleman friend. "You know how revolutionaries can be once they gain an upper hand—anyone and everyone who doesn't quite fit in with their ideals risks facing their firing squads. And with you being a foreign national who worked for the *Comptoir National d'Achats et de Distribution*, I'd say you'd run a higher risk than most."

Frosell furrowed his brow at his friend's comment, a look of consternation on his face; why would Admiral Dumesnil bring that up now, after more than five years?

"That's foolish talk," Marie countered. "You know Oscar never even took up that position." She gave the admiral her best disarming smile. "All thanks to the Germans, of course."

"Is that something you'd like to debate in front of a firing squad, Oscar," Madame Dumesnil chipped in, "or with your own people, who are obliged to be more sympathetic?"

The admiral checked his fob watch. It was an ornate, gold-plated affair, which hung from a thick chain attached to his belt. "Swedish national or not, I'd strongly suggest you at least speak to your consulate. My good friend there will agree to see you immediately and help you relocate to somewhere safer. Just until things blow over in the city, of course." He fished about in his pocket and produced a stark white card.

Out of politeness, Frosell took the card from his friend, one eyebrow raised at the name he read there. He slipped it into his pocket.

"Ask for Swedish General Consul Raoul Nordling," Admiral Dumesnil instructed. "And be sure to tell him that I sent you." The Dumesnils were close friends with Raoul Nordling, the man history would later credit as saving Paris. Legend a few months hence would be—mostly put forth by Nordling himself and perpetuated by the likes of the Dumesnils—that Nordling would single-handedly persuade Dietrich von Choltitz not to destroy the city.

"We really must be going, my darling," Madame Dumesnil urged her husband. "I'll go get Alla; she will be staying with us tonight." Far too many people had disappeared in Paris of late for Madame Dumesnil's comfort. And even with Commandante Alla being a respected major in the women's section of the French Revolutionary Air Force, both the Germans and the resistance were apt these days to shoot first and ask questions later.

"It's been a wonderful evening, Oscar." The admiral shook Frosell's hand. "Please, promise me you will give some thought about talking to Nordling? He's a decent man, and he will take good care of you and your family."

Frosell nodded, a light sprinkling of ash tumbling like miniature snowflakes from the glowing end of his cigarette. "Thank you, I will," he said. "But right now, all I'm thinking of is enjoying my holiday; this time tomorrow we will be in Cosne! I honestly can't believe it's been a year since we were last there."

And with that, the Dumesnils were bustling out into the Paris night to where their nervous driver awaited; the evening was getting dangerously late.

CHAPTER TWO

Cosne-Cours-sur-Loire, Central France. Summer 1944.

"Are we there yet, Father?" Heddy asked from the back seat of the car, her voice sleepy.

"Almost," Frosell told her. They had more than an hour of driving time to go, but he knew his daughter's impatience all too well.

Marie was sound asleep in the passenger seat beside him. Her body was slumped against the car's door, her head—cushioned by a blue rolled-up sweater—rested against its window and knocked gently upon the glass each time they hit a slight bump in the road.

Frosell had gotten his family up, dressed, ready, and on the road at dawn; he was a firm believer in early starts. The customary cigarette holder pinched between his lips, leather driving gloves gripping the wheel of his beloved black '37 Berliet Dauphine, Frosell was relishing the freedom of the open road. As much as he enjoyed life in Paris, it always felt good to be free of the city every now and then—perhaps even more so in recent months, with the increase in fighting between the Germans and de Gaulle.

They had a driver on call, of course, but Frosell preferred to take the annual family road trip under his own steam. He preferred to be the master of his own destiny and enjoy the much-treasured time to build memories with his beloved family.

Aimee Claire, his ever-reliable secretary and general assistant, was taking good care of the apartment, Younker, and Frosell's business affairs. She was a smart, capable woman whom Frosell trusted with everything he held dear, including the vast wealth he had cosseted within the formidable walls of his Rue Dufrenoy home. He'd left her with strict instructions—as he did every year—to only call him in the event of a dire emergency, and nothing short of the Allies bombing Paris into the ground would do.

They'd be staying at the Gîte du Vieux Château, as they did every year. Frosell loved the place for its rustic simplicity and understated luxury, although the latter element had waned somewhat as the inevitable shortages brought about by the war had taken their toll. Still, it was a wonderful getaway for the Frosell family and a welcome retreat for Marie and Heddy especially. Frosell knew his daughter just *adored* staying at the tiny castle, from where the family explored the timeless beauty of the Loire valley.

Cosne lay 118 miles due south of Paris, a drive that took at least three hours, more if Frosell decided to make a detour off the beaten track to delight his family with some curiosity or another. This time, though, he'd decided it would be wise to stick to the main roads. It was rumored the countryside was now prone to sporadic outbursts of fighting, along with the occasional bombing raids and haphazardly scattered land mines; the risk simply wasn't worth it.

They arrived in Cosne late morning. The air was still crisp and clean, the sun spreading its welcome warmth from a blue, cloudless sky. Frosell drove by what remained of the *Musee de la Loire*, which sat on the outskirts of the town and had always been a welcome sign that the vacation was about to begin.

Frosell had loved visiting the small museum back in its heyday; the place had been a veritable cabinet of curiosities back then, crammed to the rafters with historical artifacts, peculiar curios, and valuables from every corner of the globe. Across the years, he had become good friends with the curator, Emile Fernand-Dubois, and often would spend entire days of his vacation in the place listening intently as Monsieur Fernand-Dubois regaled him with fantastical tales of his travels abroad as he gathered together his eclectic collection. In fact, the assortment of oddities had expanded so much that the museum had been forced to move in 1937 from the twin rooms at the town hall to its new home by the Pont de Loire bridge.

Sadly, the move had proved to be the musee's undoing, as the invading German forces had strategically bombed the bridge in the early days of 1940. Rather unfortunately, Mademoiselle Fernand-Dubois had been killed in the raid, as the museum was almost completely leveled along with the bridge, and many of the musee's formidable collections within were destroyed.

Frosell hoped one day they would rebuild the musee. He knew Heddy would share his delight and enthusiasm for the oddities and ancient things it harbored. It saddened him that his daughter had never gotten to see the place, which had reminded him so much of their own home.

Thoughts of the Paris apartment floated through Frosell's mind as he drove the final mile or so to the Château, a melancholic reverie buoyed along by thoughts of the fate of the little museum. So far, the presence of the Germans in Paris had been a safeguard for his own vast collection of valuables: gold, platinum, works of art, gems, and the near-priceless stamp collections he'd built up after his mother, the countess Artemis da Ponte, had bequeathed her fortune to him; she had exhibited quite the extraordinary eye for exquisite artwork, antique furniture, and all things of rare beauty.

Had Paris suffered the same fate as many European cities throughout the war—Dresden, Hamburg, London, Hull, Warsaw, the list seemed endless—then the Frosell fortune would have surely perished. Either that, or he would have been forced to move it out into the French countryside, or possibly across the Swiss border; both options came with the very real danger of highway robbery or looting. As contradictory as it may have been, the occupying forces had been the true protectors of Oscar Frosell, his family, and their vast wealth. Frosell would often feel guilty at the odd dichotomy. Which was precisely why he had absolutely no intention of leaving Rue Dufrenoy—despite Dumesnil's dire warnings of gloom, doom, and Allied forces.

And what exactly had the pompous ass meant by, *and with you being a foreign national who worked at the Comptoir National d'Achats et de Distribution*? Why on earth would the admiral bring it up now, after five years and a job that never really was? The almost job had been shortly after the Germans launched their lightning attack on France in 1939. As the Paris streets echoed to the sound of Nazi jackboots, the French Ministry of Production had formed the official organization known as C.N.A.D. Its role was to organize France's motor fuel and generator gas markets for efficient delivery to the Germans, all under the watchful eye of Marshal Pètain and his collaborators.

Frosell had been contacted by one of Pètain's people and offered a position completing the contracts between the French producers and their German buyers. It was something he was fully permitted to do as a Swedish national, entirely in keeping with his neutral government's official policy. His salary was to have been an almost nominal two francs per ton delivered. For Frosell, though, it was not about the money, it was about doing whatever he could to keep his family and their fortune safe.

It was the Germans who broke the contract. Before Frosell had even had the opportunity to spend his first day at his C.N.A.D. desk, it was announced quite publicly they did not want a foreigner to hold such a sensitive position; the Nazis then tore up his contract. And that had been that. Frosell had barely given the matter a second thought. Until Admiral Dumesnil happened to mention it at the party, of course.

The question still stood, buzzing around Frosell's mind like some troublesome insect. Why would Dumesnil bring it up now? It was something that would prey on Frosell's mind the entire vacation.

Frosell made a mental note to call Aimee Claire the minute they were settled at the Château. It would put his own mind to rest, and he would ask her to keep a close eye on the good admiral, his strange wife, and that precocious daughter of theirs.

Frosell was still pondering the admiral's counsel when he swung the Berliet into the small driveway that sat at the front of the Gîte du Vieux Château. Immediately, the sight of the beautiful little castle lifted his heart.

"We're here!" Heddy announced from the back seat with absolute joy in her voice.

"Yes, we are." Frosell smiled at the little girl, taking great delight in her excitement. "I told you we wouldn't be too much longer."

Marie stirred, rubbing the sleep from the corners of her eyes. "We're here already, Oscar?" she asked.

Frosell smiled, took a long draw on his cigarette, and gave his wife's knee a fond pat. "We are indeed, my dear. And thank you for your company."

Marie Frosell offered her husband a sheepish grin and winked at Heddy. She'd slept through the entire journey.

For as much as she loved home back in the city—after all, it was all she had known in her short life—Heddy loved the Château and the rolling, verdant countryside that surrounded it. She loved the long, sweeping bends of the Loire that sliced through the greenery, and the days spent drifting along on its lazy current in the boat Father leased or picnicking on its gently sloping banks. The place was quiet that year; with all the talk of the Allied invasion, not too many people were vacationing. Oftentimes, Heddy felt as if she and her parents had the entire Loire valley to themselves.

At the miniature castle that was to be home for the summer, Heddy could so easily lose herself in her imagination—her *daydreaming*, as Mother liked to call it. Heddy imagined herself a soldier, a famous pilot of the resistance like Commandante Dumesnil, or a princess living in a high tower and safe from the grenades and sporadic crackle of distant gunfire, which some nights didn't seem all that distant.

Heddy was a child more than content in the company of her own imagination. She would make up stories, tall tales, and adventures to keep herself entertained as she trailed along everywhere with her parents. Father often said young Heddy might grow up to be a famous writer someday; she just needed to find the right story to tell.

Friends were few and far between for Heddy, especially since many of her erstwhile school friends had fled Paris. Her father would occasionally receive a visitor who happened to have a child around Heddy's age, and she would have a playmate for an afternoon. The norm to Heddy was for parents to have their children tag along everywhere they went and not be let out of their sight for more than one minute. In fact, Heddy struggled to remember a time when she had not been in her parents' company as they perused art galleries, ate out in Paris's finest restaurants, and visited friends. She even went along to some of Father's business meetings with accountants and attorneys. All of those were terribly dry affairs, especially as she was never furnished with a book or a toy to keep her occupied; the quiet, painfully polite Heddy Frosell was forever alone with her vivid imagination.

The vacation flew by fast, as such things often did, and the time came to prepare for the Frosells to return to Paris. For their last night in Cosne, Father suggested they try out a new restaurant that had recently opened up in the small town. It was the rather grand sounding *l'Orchidèe Royale*, a tiny, family-run establishment just off the town's main square. After a vacation of revisiting favorite spots, Heddy was almost as excited as her father to try out something new.

Heddy's little chest puffed up with pride as all heads turned when Father walked into the cozy restaurant. The handful of patrons eyed him as someone obviously quite important, and the wait staff all but fell over themselves to find Oscar Frosell and his family the perfect seat in the restaurant. It was not like they were old friends or local dignitaries; there was just something in the way Heddy's father carried himself that inspired awe in people. After all, this was the man who had stubbornly refused to flee Paris when the Germans arrived and had remained steadfast in his resolve to protect his family, property, and riches.

Oscar Frosell was, indeed, a most imposing figure. He carried himself with the dignified poise of a man to be reckoned with and, as such, was one who could never possibly go unnoticed. Tall, handsome, with distinctive looks and that ever-present ornate cigarette holder, Frosell had about him a definite air of authority that everyone automatically looked up to, even before learning who he was or listening to his intelligent, engaging way of speaking. From her earliest memories, Heddy had known her father to be an incredibly smart man, and she often thought he was possibly the cleverest person in the whole wide world. He was entirely fluent in seven different languages and was a total perfectionist in absolutely everything he did, be it business or pleasure, to the point of being infuriatingly pedantic. The little girl also knew from personal experience her father was also a man for whom failure was simply never an option, and that he somehow managed to succeed in everything he turned his hand to, without fail. As such, Oscar Frosell was incredibly accomplished at painting, calligraphy, and woodwork as well as all of his business endeavors—literally everything the man touched, he had to be the best at it.

Unfortunately, as a consequence of how driven and success focused he was, Frosell could never even imagine accepting not winning when he knew he had right on his side; it was a trait that often bordered on obsession and one that ensured he never gave up, even when things looked hopeless.

Frosell also demanded nothing less than a hundred percent from everyone else around him—be it business associates, employees, house staff, or family—in every thing they did. Of course, that fearsome attitude extended to his daughter who, even at her tender young age, spent a great deal of her time attempting to impress the man she admired to the point of hero worship. From her earliest recollections, Heddy had grown up being told by her father that if she wasn't the best in whatever she decided to turn her hand to, she simply wasn't good enough. It was a cold, harsh indoctrination that was to stick with the impressionable little girl and give her a deep-rooted inferiority complex that she would never, ever be good enough, nor would she ever feel she was; it was one that would last throughout her entire life.

Perched upon the simple wooden chair between her parents, Heddy studied the specials board—handwritten in a spidery, chalky scrawl—while Father ordered off the menu, as he often did when they ate out. Although l'Orchidèe served escargots and frogs' legs, Heddy opted for the cassoulet and a baguette. Bread had become rather the rare treat in France, as most of it was sent to the men fighting at the front. Mother ordered the coq au vin, and Father treated himself to something with veal in a red wine sauce that looked quite spectacular.

It was such a delight for Heddy to see her father so relaxed that night. He'd appeared more distracted than usual throughout their vacation; there was just something in the way he'd draw on his cigarettes with extra gusto, or how she would catch him gazing off into the distance as if he were deep in thought or off on some fantastical imaginary adventure of his own.

Heddy listened intently as Father made small talk with her mother. It lifted her heart to see how the two of them touched hands and laughed like love-struck newlyweds. Her father was reminiscing about the time he'd gotten to hear Enrico Caruso live in concert, and how a dear friend had arranged for them to meet after the show. Caruso had always been one of Father's favorite opera singers, and most evenings the Frosells' plush apartment would be filled with the tenor's rich, smooth voice. Heddy had inherited her father's love of opera and the classics; so much so, even at the tender age of five years old she recognized *L'elisir d'amore* playing softly in the restaurant. The proprietor had put on the record at Father's request, and that particular song, as sung by the great Caruso, never failed to place a smile upon his lips and a happy sparkle in Mother's eye.

Heddy, of course, remained silent. She knew to speak only when Father asked her a direct question, for polite little girls were to be seen and not heard; Heddy knew the rule all too well. She was more than content in the boundless realms of her imagination and would wander off on flights of fancy as her parents made small talk and enjoyed the delicious food; the little girl was always more than happy in their company as well as her own.

She was also feeling a little homesick and looking forward to returning home to Paris, her own bed, Younker, and familiar surroundings. She was even looking forward to Aimee Claire and that stern, clinically efficient way she had about her wherever Heddy was concerned. Heddy didn't even mind the thought of lying awake in the dark of the night listening to the staccato rattle of gunfire and having to crawl on hands and knees by the windows to avoid the threat of stray bullets whenever a skirmish erupted in the streets outside the apartment. She had grown used to spending many a night in the apartment's chilly basement when the sirens sounded, where she would sleep on an old cot that had been down there since the day they'd moved in.

War was all Heddy had known, having been born the year the Second World War had broken out; she often puzzled as to why the Great War was still referred to as "the war to end all wars" when here they were again. To Heddy, shortages and curfews, blackouts, and the mysterious disappearance of a neighbor or two were commonplace and held little fear. It was all *character building*, as Father liked to call it.

The evening floated wonderfully along for Oscar Frosell, Marie, and their painfully polite, quiet little girl. The wine flowed, soft laughter drifted around the bijou restaurant, and exceptionally good food was enjoyed. It was quite the most perfect end to the Frosells' summer vacation.

And not one of them could have anticipated the beginning of the nightmare awaiting them upon their return to Paris.

CHAPTER THREE

Paris. Early August 1944.

"Marie! Oscar!" Madame Dumesnil appeared from the doorway of the Rue Dufrenoy building the very moment the Frosells' car eased to a gentle stop at the curbside. Towering above them was the magnificent sandstone façade of the apartment; the black wrought-iron balcony railings adorning each window glinted in the sunshine of the early afternoon.

"Quickly, quickly!" She ushered Marie and Heddy from the car with panic etched in her shrill voice.

Marie pulled Heddy tight to her skirts. A hint of fear danced in her eyes. "What on earth—"

"Inside! Quickly, quickly!" the admiral's wife urged. She grasped Marie's hand and all but dragged her toward the apartment.

"Oscar, my friend!" Admiral Dumesnil stepped toward the Berliet and tugged the door open, as if he were some grandiose valet.

Frosell stepped from the car with a frosty expression upon his face. "Monsieur Dumesnil?" he said as the admiral took his arm and followed his good lady wife. "What's the meaning of all this?" Frosell protested. "Has something happened to the apartment?"

The admiral glanced nervously along Rue Dufrenoy. His eyes narrowed as he espied a movement in the distance. "It's not safe here, Oscar. You should not have come back to the city," he said with urgency as he maneuvered Frosell into the apartment building. Alla stood there in the vestibule, resplendent in her uniform, quite obviously doing her utmost not to appear as if she'd been waiting for them.

Frosell allowed the admiral to escort him to the apartment. While he was immune to the Dumesnils' drama, Frosell was eager to make sure all was well up there even though he knew Aimee Claire would have contacted him had anything untoward happened while he was away.

"Are you going to tell me what all this is about?" he quizzed Dumesnil as they hurried along with Marie, Heddy, Alla, and Madame Dumesnil in tow.

"Have you not heard, Oscar?" the admiral snapped. "The uprising has gained strength in Paris ever since the Allies took Normandy."

Frosell sighed. Of course he'd kept himself abreast of the events in Europe—especially Paris; Cosne was not a million miles away, and it did have newspapers and radio! "Is *that* what's worrying you?" he asked Dumesnil, with impatience showing through in his voice. He slowed his step as the urgency dissipated somewhat. On their return to Paris, Frosell had spotted the telltale signs of increased fighting between the occupying Germans and the resistance: uneven trails of machine gun bullet holes in the brickwork, boarded-up storefronts, even fading bloodstains on the damp streets. While a familiar sight to him, there had definitely been more than when they'd departed just two short months before. The signs of violence were also much closer to Rue Dufrenoy.

"Of course it's a worry!" Madame Dumesnil's shrill voice echoed about the wide hallway. "They've been robbing stores and houses, Oscar, and people are going missing!" She sounded close to tears, her footsteps uneven as she walked alongside Marie and Heddy. "One hears such terrible things! Alla has told us such awful tales of looting, torture, and even murder! There have been bodies floating in the Seine! Tell him, Alla."

"My mother is right," Alla added her gravitas. "Since the Allies took the beaches in June, there are factions who are taking the opportunity to plunder and deal with those people who they don't much care for. Collaborators, especially."

Frosell bristled at the sound of that word. He turned around to face the commandante as she narrowed her eyes at him. "Then we will be just fine," he said through gritted teeth.

"Your family is not safe here, Oscar," the admiral reiterated as they arrived at the front door to the Frosells' apartment. "You are not a French national, and that is always going to raise suspicion." He took in a long, deep breath. "And then there's your Achats et la Distribution business . . ."

Frosell pushed open the door to the apartment and rounded on Dumesnil. "You know that's all just nonsense!" he growled.

"I'm just concerned about you, my old fr—"

"Then show your concern by *not* bringing that subject up again!" It was not often Oscar Frosell raised his voice. On the occasions he did, however, it could strike fear into even the hardest of hearts. "Just how many more times must I explain to you? I—"

"Didn't take up the position?" Dumesnil cut in. "Yes, yes, Oscar. *We* know that to be the case. But what of the underground, or the Allies? What happens when someone comes across the paper trail showing your collusion with Germany?"

"There was no *collusion*, Admiral." Frosell squared up to his self-important friend. "It was a job I was offered and never even happened. It's as simple as that!"

They walked down along the hallway to be greeted by Younker and Aimee Claire, who appeared even sterner than was her usual demeanor. Heddy scampered off to play with her dog, the pair clearly delighted to be reunited after so long apart, and Frosell, Marie, and the Dumesnils made themselves comfortable in the drawing room.

Frosell poured each of them a stiff Cognac and took a contemplative moment, gazing out over his beloved city at the pleasant greenery of the Parc de Bagatelle; it was difficult for him to believe that just a few short hours ago he had been enjoying the unrivaled beauty of the Loire valley.

"Monsieur Frosell"—it was Alla who broke the awkward silence— "do you honestly believe de Gaulle's people will bother to ask if you actually sat behind the desk at C.N.A.D?" She took a long, noisy sip at her brandy. "Need I also remind you that you are a foreign national? You know you won't be afforded protection by the French government?"

Frosell fixed the commandante with an icy stare. He lit up another cigarette using the glowing cherry of the stub he'd almost smoked through, and then swapped the two over in the holder. He took in a deep lungful of the acrid smoke and exhaled it slowly. "I am *painfully* aware of the fact, thank you," he replied. "But I have resided in Paris for many years now. I also have nothing to hide or be ashamed of." He glanced across the room at Marie, who was looking increasingly worried; her post-vacation *joie de vivre* was well and truly dissipating.

"That's all well and good in peace time," Admiral Dumesnil threw in. "But we are at war, Oscar, and the rules are much different."

"There is talk of a general strike," Alla said. "The Germans will be routed, and de Gaulle will retake Paris." She shuffled uneasily in the antique Louis XV armchair. "I am not supposed to be telling you this, Monsieur Frosell, but I know I can trust your discretion."

Madame Dumesnil leaned across to Marie and took hold of her hand. "We are only afraid for your safety," she said, her voice quiet and trembling. "I couldn't bear to think of what may happen to you. Or to poor, dear Heddy."

Alla looked Frosell dead in the eyes. Her stony face gave little away, and Frosell thought that for a usually attractive young woman she had a certain knack for showing her ugly side. "Collaborators will be the first ones up against the wall when we take back Paris, Monsieur Frosell." The commandante's voice was cold and uncaring. "Neutral country or not, on paper at least you will be seen as a collaborator."

"Is this true, Oscar?" Marie asked. She was close to tears.

Frosell shook his head and took in a long, deep draw of his cigarette, its glowing tip reflecting on his sun-kissed cheeks. "I very much doubt it," he told her. A faint tremor in his voice gave away the soupçon of uncertainty gnawing away at the back of his mind. "But as the admiral said, this is wartime, and people may not act as rationally as you might expect them to." With that, Frosell shot Alla a withering glance. He was angry she had managed to upset his dear wife with such ruthless and deliberate efficiency.

"Then you should take our advice, Oscar," Madame Dumesnil said. "At the very least you could meet with Monsieur Nordling, if only to put poor Marie's mind at rest."

Frosell looked into his wife's tear-filled eyes and he felt his resolve eroding. "I guess it wouldn't hurt to meet with the man," he conceded with a half smile. In the dark recesses of his mind he cursed the Dumesnils and their interfering ways.

Dumesnil drained his glass and scrambled to his feet. "Then it is decided," he announced. "Come along, my friend."

Frosell eyed the admiral with some amusement. Had he not known any better, he'd swear the admiral, his good lady wife, and their taciturn daughter had carefully planned out this entire thing. "Now?"

"There's no time like the present," Dumesnil told him. "The resistance and the Allies are not going to wait around for the great Oscar Frosell to sort out his affairs—no matter how wealthy he is!" With this, the admiral attempted a half laugh, which came out as more of a snort. "Raoul will be at the consulate shortly. We can meet him there."

Frosell opened his mouth to protest, but an anxious glance from Marie advised him otherwise. "It looks like you win, Admiral." He gave the Dumesnils his best disarming smile.

"There's no *winning* involved," Madame Dumesnil said. "This is for the safety of your family, Oscar, and you must promise us you will listen to what Monsieur Nordling has to tell you."

Frosell nodded and made his way out of the room with the admiral hot on his heels, scampering like some eager puppy. "We can take my car," the admiral told him as they left. "I have my driver waiting by the rear entrance."

"Thank you, Admiral," Frosell replied, "but I would rather take my own car." Frosell knew where the consulate was, of course, and didn't care much for the admiral's driving.

"As you wish, Oscar." Dumesnil appeared a tad put out. "You can follow me there." And so saying, the admiral ushered Oscar Frosell from his own apartment as if he were a common criminal.

CHAPTER FOUR

The Swedish Consulate, Paris. August 1944.

The gray, stone-fronted consulate itself was beautiful enough. Yet it was quite unremarkable among the historic buildings of Paris, a city inhabited by some of the world's greatest architecture. Frosell had visited his country's consulate before, of course, but never under such inauspicious circumstances as this.

Something about the Dumesnils' insistences didn't quite sit right with him, especially as he'd been ruminating over the comments the admiral had made before he and his family had departed for Cosne. It was always quite possible the admiral, Madame Dumesnil, and their daughter had the Frosell family's best interests and safety at heart. But Frosell's well-honed gut instinct as a shrewd businessman was advising him to proceed with caution.

"Monsieur Nordling will be with you shortly," the gray-haired lady behind the reception desk informed Frosell and the admiral. "Please take a seat."

The vestibule was stark and, with nothing to adorn the gray stone walls, it echoed with every footstep and hushed conversation. All of the valuable artwork had been removed and shipped back to Sweden nearly the second Hitler's forces had set foot on French soil; the Swedes knew the Nazis were unlikely to be all that respectful of a country's neutrality.

"Thank you for allowing me to bring you here," the admiral said to Frosell as they made themselves at home on the uncomfortable wooden chairs. He kept his voice to a whisper lest it be carried along through the vaulted ceilings. "You will see it makes good sense, Oscar. Raoul will make sure you do the right thing; he only has your family's best interests at heart."

Frosell narrowed his eyes at the admiral. He puffed on the fresh cigarette he'd just lit up. "You have already discussed my family with the consul?"

"Only in passing." Dumesnil sounded a tad defensive at Frosell's accusation. "And only because I am worried about you, my friend." He patted Frosell's knee as if he were a small child in need of reassurance. "Raoul Nordling is a good friend of mine, and you know how good friends talk?"

Frosell sighed. He was not in any kind of mood for Dumesnil to regale him once again with stories of his friendship with the man.

"Ah! Raoul!" the admiral exclaimed and jumped to his feet. "It's so good to see you again!"

Raoul Nordling shuffled his way across the consulate atrium. He had one arm outstretched in greeting and the other stuffed deep in the pants pocket of his slate gray, three-piece suit. He shook hands with Dumesnil with a faint smile dancing across his thin lips. "It is always good to see you, Admiral," he said.

"This is my good friend Oscar Frosell." Dumesnil made the obvious introduction.

"Of course," Nordling replied. He greeted Frosell with a firm, if somewhat slightly damp, handshake. "You need no introduction, Mr. Frosell." His thick, growling voice made his jowls wobble. "The most renowned Swedish businessman in Paris is well known to everyone here at the consulate."

Frosell studied Nordling. Having only seen the man from a distance before that day, he thought him to be a touch taller and rounder than expected. "Thank you for taking the time to meet with us." Frosell did his best not to show his impatience toward Dumesnil. "I can only hope that it is not wasted. Admiral Dumesnil can be quite persuasive—as I'm sure you are aware."

Nordling let out a hearty guffaw, and his body wobbled beneath his expensive suit. The receptionist shot him a disapproving look. "Painfully so, Mr. Frosell, painfully so," the consul agreed. "But on this occasion he has advised you well."

The joviality came to an abrupt stop, and Nordling's face adopted its usual dour expression. His eyes took on a furtive expression as they darted around the atrium walls as if he were looking for someone. "It's best we don't talk here," he whispered. "Walls have ears, don't you know?" He turned his back on his two guests and strode off with his Italian shoes—polished to a mirror finish—click-clacking on the cold stone floor.

Dumesnil took off after Nordling. Frosell followed on as the consul led the way through a side door and into the maze of hallways and small, featureless offices secreted within the heart of the consulate. Frosell puffed impatiently on his cigarette as he strode along. He was already reaching into his pocket for the next one—this whole scenario was becoming a little too cloak and dagger for his liking.

Nordling came to a sudden stop by a narrow, shabby door with yellowed, flaking paint that led to a small office. He shoved the door open and steered Frosell and the admiral inside. He pulled the door closed behind them, struggling to make the warped wood fit into its frame. He then twisted the latch to lock them all inside.

"Sit. Please." Nordling pointed to a trio of rickety wooden chairs that sat around a round, metal table in the center of the room. "We can talk freely here," he said. His eyes flicked toward the door, as if he were expecting guests.

Nordling sat forward in his chair. Its old wooden frame creaked under his bulk. "You are no longer safe in Paris, Monsieur Frosell," he said bluntly.

"What are you talking about?" Frosell asked. He was becoming increasingly irritated by the whole surreptitious business.

Nordling bridged his fingers and held them beneath his nose. "I am advising you, as your country's consulate, to get your family out of Paris. For your own safety."

"The Vichy regime is about to fall, Oscar," Dumesnil added. "Once the general strike begins, it will only be a matter of time." He gave Frosell what was no doubt intended to be a comforting smile.

"With that, and once the Germans are gone, there will be nothing to protect you."

Frosell bristled. He knew where this was leading. "Protect me from what, Monsieur Nordling?"

"Please, call me Raoul," Nordling insisted. "Once that's all over and done with, the victors will be looking to rout out everyone who may have colluded with the Nazis, Oscar." He leaned back in his creaky old chair. "Of course, there will be those who will use it as an excuse to plunder what they can and line their own pockets." He gave a derisory snort. "Spoils of war and all that."

Frosell considered arguing with the consul about the false accusation of collaboration but decided instead to hold his tongue; the sooner this meeting was over and he could return home, the better.

"I have a place for you to go," Nordling persisted. "It's not quite so grand as you are used to, but it's on the outskirts of the city and is quite safe." He pulled out a small, crumpled piece of paper from his pants pocket and placed it on the metal tabletop.

"I'm not going anywhere." Frosell couldn't help but protest; the officious consul was riling him now. "I will not leave my home."

"Ah, yes," Nordling said as he smoothed out the paper so Frosell could see the address was typed upon it. "The famous Frosell Rue Dufrenoy apartment. I can understand why you would be reluctant to leave, Oscar. I hear that it is like a small museum."

This place resembles nothing less than a small museum. Wouldn't you agree?

"It would only be temporary," Dumesnil added, "until all of this has blown over."

"And there is no need for you to worry about your apartment and possessions, Oscar," Nordling said with a warm smile. "I'll take care of all of that myself. I will personally have it sealed under the protection of the Swedish consulate."

Frosell shook his head. He'd been in business long enough to know when he was being railroaded toward a *fait accompli*. "I thank you for your concern, Raoul, but I do not intend to—"

Nordling waved a hand to silence Frosell. He fished about in an inside pocket of his tailored suit and pulled out another, larger sheet of paper. He laid it out on the scratched tabletop.

Frosell and the admiral leaned over to better see the faded handwritten scrawl, which filled most of the paper.

"This is a copy obtained from the Resistance by French intelligence. As you can see, Oscar, the safety of you, your wife, and child can no longer be guaranteed in Paris," Nordling told Frosell. "You must leave immediately."

What Oscar Frosell read on the crinkled, unassuming scrap of paper put the fear of God into him and chilled his very soul. A sick, leaden lump formed in the pit of his stomach, and the acid sting of bile rose up in his throat. "Oh, dear Lord," he groaned.

Nordling's single sheet of paper contained a list of Parisians, some of whom Frosell knew through his business dealings, who were suspected of collaboration and profiteering under the occupation. His name was on there, of course, at the very top of the right-hand column. Directly above it, written in hasty scribble, were the words, *Vive la Resistance!*

"I have to go." Frosell's cracked voice was filled with dread. He plucked both pieces of paper from the table and clutched them tightly, as if his life depended upon them. "I have to go *now.*"

Frosell drove the Berliet hard through the Paris streets, much harder than he'd driven her before. He was a great believer in respecting the finer things in life, and the car was one of his prized possessions; however, there were far more pressing matters weighing upon Frosell's mind as he ignored the speed restrictions along Boulevard Lannes to take the Boulevard Flanderin shortcut he knew so well. As he drove, all Frosell could see in his mind's eye was the hastily scribbled note the Swedish general consul had fished out of that expensive suit of his, and for the first time for as long as he could remember, he genuinely feared for his family's safety.

It was with great relief Frosell swung the car onto Rue Dufrenoy and found the street to be almost empty; he'd half expected to have arrived home only to find Nordling's warnings had come all too late and there was a welcoming committee of de Gaulle's soldiers and gendarmes awaiting his return. But no, other than the Lafont's black Citroen parked up along the street, the place was remarkably devoid of vehicles.

Frosell pulled the Berliet to a halt outside the apartment building; the tires made a terrible noise as they skidded along the street and left twin black lines behind them. Without stopping to lock the car, Frosell leapt out and raced to the apartment.

"Pack a bag," Frosell barked at Marie as he dashed through the hallway with barely a cursory glance at Aimee Claire.

"We have not yet *unpacked* our bags," Marie replied. A look of grave concern spread across her face. It was rare to see her husband in such a state; he had raced into the apartment as if the devil himself were on his tail. "Is there something wrong, Oscar?"

"Where's the child?" Frosell ignored his wife's question and brushed by her on the way to the master bedroom. "Aimee Claire! Have you seen Heddy?"

Marie followed him, her face flushed. "You're scaring me, Oscar. Are you going to tell me what's going on?" she demanded.

Frosell continued to stuff clothes into an overnight bag as he turned around. "I'll explain later, Marie. For now, just please do as I ask and pack a few things for you and Heddy. We need to leave immediately."

Marie opened her mouth to speak, but a stern glance from her husband advised her otherwise. "Heddy!" she called out as she bustled from the room, her heart lying heavy in her chest.

Frosell turned his attention to the pair of safes hiding in the corner of the bedroom. Turning to the first one, and with well-practiced efficiency, he twisted the dial on its cold steel front. With a resounding *click*, the safe's door swung open, its meticulously oiled hinges making no sound at all. Frosell grabbed what cash he had in there, ignoring the gold and platinum ingots that he much preferred instead of paper money; his father had taught him well to be wary of cash money, a warning borne out during Germany's prewar days of hyperinflation.

Frosell stuffed the cash into his bag and slammed the safe door shut, the loud, metallic clang flashing stark images of prison cells in his mind. Then, as habit dictated, he spun the dial around three times and pulled on the safe's handle—just to be sure.

Satisfied his gold, platinum, gemstones, and rare stamps were secure, Frosell grabbed his overnight bag from the bed and made his way out.

To his relief, Marie had located the child and had her waiting by the front door with her own little bag of clothes clutched in her hand. "She wants to say goodbye to Younker," Marie explained.

Frosell glanced down at his daughter's tearful, bewildered face and his heart sank. "He'll be fine," he offered. "It's not as if we're going away for long—and Aimee Claire will take good care of him."

"Don't you worry, Heddy." The secretary chipped in with what Frosell was sure was meant to be a reassuring smile. Instead, the woman's anxiety shone through, and it appeared as more of a grimace. "I'll be sure to give Younker an extra big hug for you."

Frosell turned to his secretary. "We must be going," he said as calmly as he could manage. "Take care of things while we're gone."

Aimee Claire gave a somber nod. "Do you know how long—?"

"Not long at all," Frosell cut her off. "We'll be back before you have time to miss us." He gave her his fondest smile and ushered Marie and Heddy out of the apartment.

Aimee Claire watched the family leave, her heart sinking as the door closed gently behind them. She wasn't to know it, but that would be the last time she'd ever see Monsieur Frosell and the family she'd grown to love.

Oscar Frosell's car had barely turned the corner onto Rue de la Faisanderie before a half dozen police cars hurtled down Rue Dufrenoy and screeched to a stop outside the apartment. Curtains twitched all along the street as the gendarmes clambered from their vehicles and swarmed *en masse* into the apartment building; a handful of the Frosells' less apprehensive neighbors stepped from their front doors to sate their inquisitive natures at the sudden burst of activity, the likes of which had not been seen before along that quiet Parisian road.

A meticulously polished, gleaming black Renault Juvaquatre pulled up behind the haphazardly parked police cars. It eased to a gentle stop with more finesse than the gendarmes had managed. The door to the apartment building opened, and a trio of fearsome-looking police nationale officers escorted out all of the members of Oscar Frosell's staff: the chauffeur, the cook and her assistants, and the trio of maids. They also ushered out Oscar's plump, faithful secretary; they frog marched her down the stairs from the second floor with her wrists secured behind her back with clinking steel handcuffs. The poor woman was crying uncontrollably; her tear-streaked face was quite the pitiful sight as she attempted to reason with the officers, who ignored her pitiful pleas for clemency and hurried her to one of their awaiting vehicles.

Raoul Nordling stepped from his car once Aimee Claire was safely secured in the back of the police vehicle and driven away. Easing his broad frame from within its tight confines, he made his way across to the apartment building, let himself in, and took the stairs up to the Frosells' apartment.

"Bonjour," an officer greeted the Swedish general consul with a smile.

"Ah, bonjour," Nordling replied. "Are we all done in here?" He pointed at the Frosells' front door, which stood half open. Inside, he could make out the myriad policemen—*flics* as he'd heard the locals call them on many an occasion—searching the vast apartment, although what they could possibly be looking for was beyond him.

"Oui. Almost done, monsieur."

"I think you *are* done." Nordling's impatience rose to the surface of his usually congenial façade. He waved an important-looking sheet of paper under the gendarme's nose. "Need I remind you this is not French property and is under diplomatic protection of my country?" He pointed to the seal of the Swedish Consulate at the bottom of the page. "I am here to seal the property on behalf of my government."

The policeman shot the fat, dour diplomat a withering look of disdain. Nonetheless, he ordered the other agents to vacate the apartment immediately and looked on as Nordling locked the door and secured the seal in place with a quartet of brass pushpins.

CHAPTER FIVE

Abandoned Swedish Old Folks' Home, Montmartre.
September 16ᵗʰ, 1944.

It had been more than two weeks since the victorious de Gaulle gave his speech and Leclerc's French Second Armored Division paraded down the Champs Èlysèes, and yet the newspapers Frosell managed to obtain from the city were still filled with accounts of those two triumphant days. Frosell had an inkling de Gaulle himself may well have been behind the constant reporting of the routing of the occupying Germans during the general strike. From what he'd learned about the man, the general was certainly not above self-aggrandizing. Frosell read with some alarm about a remaining handful of active German snipers, some of whom had shot at the crowd from the rooftops around the Hôtel de Crillon area as de Gaulle had entered the Place de la Concorde. The papers didn't report any casualties, which Frosell hoped was not merely a propaganda exercise—he had good friends who'd gone along to witness de Gaulle's victory march.

If only half of the overly dramatic depictions of those tumultuous days in Paris were to be believed, Frosell had gotten his family out of the apartment in the nick of time: Nazi collaborators, sympathizers, and anyone even so much as *suspected* of colluding with the occupying forces had been rounded up and dumped in the prisons without even so much as a token trial. And, once the prisons were full—which took an alarmingly short space of time—the remaining unfortunates were shipped out to the concentration camps.

Of course, Frosell knew from the contacts he maintained in the city, the rounding up of the eclectic mix of undesirables was as much to do with the settling of old scores and procurement of coveted property as it was with rooting out the genuine collaborators and profiteers. From the reports, it seemed to Frosell the rounding up had intensified mere days after he, Marie, and Heddy had fled the apartment, and for that he was grateful to the Swedish general consul. Despite his initial impression of the man, Frosell considered he owed Raoul Nordling an immense debt of gratitude.

Frosell took a long draw from his cigarette and noted its glowing end was alarmingly close to the onyx holder. Since leaving the city, Frosell had found that maintaining his ready supply of cigarettes was increasingly difficult, and he'd been forced to ration himself. This he did find to be almost wonderfully ironic; throughout the war he had been able to acquire pretty much anything for a price, yet now it was all but over, he was facing shortages!

"Do you have plans for today?" Marie's voice broke her husband's reverie. "It's a nice day; I thought we could take Heddy into the countryside."

Frosell shook his head. "I'm expecting a call," he told her with a nod to the old Bakelite telephone perched on a small table next to his armchair. The phone still worked—barely—and it kept him in touch with those business acquaintances and contacts who'd not fled Paris and who were not too frightened to associate with an alleged collaborator; upon the Frosells' hasty departure, rumors, being what they were, had spread. "And besides, the child seems perfectly happy as she is." His eyes followed his daughter as she scooted by on the old tricycle he'd procured from an acquaintance in Marseilles, her little legs pumping up and down like tiny, thin pistons. It wasn't quite the shiny new one she constantly rode up and down the long, polished wood hallways at Rue Dufrenoy, but it nonetheless helped keep Heddy's fertile imagination occupied.

Heddy ignored her parents as she raced on by; she was busy being chased by a huge, winged dragon with an appetite for young princesses and had no time to stop to chat. Not that Father would have entertained her, of course; he never did when he was busy reading the newspapers. Even Mother appeared to be an annoyance to him this morning. Skillfully evading the dragon, Heddy maneuvered her white stallion into the day room. There, she hid behind the old mildewed piano until the danger had passed.

The deserted old people's home was a whole new world apart from Heddy's cosseted city life in Rue Dufrenoy. It was terribly dilapidated, with peeling wallpaper, flaky paint, and damp-warped woodwork. The roof leaked in all but a handful of rooms, and the whole place hung with a weird, dank, *old* smell Heddy guessed had little to do with the rain seeping in. Father had explained to her they'd moved the old people out of the home not long after the Germans invaded France. Those with money had fled to the neutral safety of Switzerland, while the less affluent were spirited away into the surrounding French countryside. Heddy couldn't begin to think what the Germans would want with a bunch of old people, but she hoped they were all safe and sound nevertheless.

As much as she loved her old apartment, her toys, and her dog, Heddy loved the dozens upon dozens of rooms to explore at the home. She also delighted in having the long, crooked hallways to race along, and the huge windows, which looked out onto the sprawling green of the gardens. Of course, she would still occasionally hear the crackle of distant gunfire and muted boom of heavy artillery as the last of the Germans put up their brave-but-foolish fight against the Allied forces. Yet somehow, the little girl felt more distanced from all of that than she had living in the center of Paris, which was, in its own way, a little safer.

Heddy clambered from her trike and hunkered down behind one of the old overstuffed sofas inhabiting the day room. Heddy could imagine the place as it used to be, back in its heyday, filled with shuffling old people—each one of them with countless memories of a life well lived and a thousand fascinating stories to tell. Sometimes, when she was feeling particularly lonely, Heddy would wish some of the *elderlies*—as mother preferred to call them—had remained at the home. That way, she would have had someone to talk to, someone to listen to *her* stories as intently as she knew she'd listen to theirs.

There came a loud knock on the front door, which startled Heddy from her reverie. Visitors were incredibly few and far between at the home, and her natural curiosity was aroused. So, satisfied the fearsome dragon would be long gone by now, Heddy mounted her trusty steed and headed out toward the main vestibule. Little did she know, but once again, her whole world was about to be turned upside down.

"What is the meaning of this?" Father's angry tone frightened Heddy a little; it wasn't often he raised his voice, but when he did, it invariably meant someone would be in serious trouble.

"I'm only Monsieur Nordling's driver, Monsieur Frosell," the smartly dressed young man replied with a distinct quiver. Oscar Frosell was a most intimidating man, even when he was not exasperated.

From behind the tall wire-and-glass cage that had once held a multitude of brightly colored songbirds for the delectation of the elderly residents, Heddy peeped out at the young driver. She thought him to be most handsome in his dark blue uniform and shiny peaked chauffeur's cap, and decided to cast him as a dashing young prince in her next tale. "I am sorry, monsieur, but I was instructed to deliver the letter, not read it." Heddy was sure she detected a hint of impertinence in the chauffeur's tone, but lucky for him, Father had other things on his mind than to mention it.

"I must speak to General Consul Nordling immediately!" Frosell threw the carefully typed letter onto the floor and stormed across to the telephone. "This simply won't do!" He picked up the receiver and began to dial, tapping his fingers with increasing impatience on the age-dulled façade as the rotary dial took its time returning to zero after each number.

Almost as if he were too afraid to speak, the driver cleared his throat. "The general consul is not in his office, Monsieur Frosell," he said.

From her hiding place, Heddy could see the poor young man was becoming quite flustered. In fact, his cheeks had flushed quite a peculiar crimson color.

"Then where is he?" Frosell demanded.

"Out of the city," the driver replied, "on diplomatic business."

Frosell slammed the receiver down on its cradle. The telephone gave out a loud *ding* noise, which Heddy rather feared might well have been its last.

Marie bustled back into the room. She was wearing the apron she reserved for baking bread; she'd taken to making her own whenever her husband could lay his hands upon a little yeast. "What is it, my dear?" she asked. "Is everything all right?"

Frosell took a long, deep draw on his cigarette, which took the stub all the way down to the holder. Fat flakes of gray ash floated down to the floor and settled there like grim snowflakes. "It's Nordling," he told his wife. "He's saying we have to move again—immediately."

"Back to Rue Dufrenoy?" Marie asked.

Heddy's heart flipped. As much as she enjoyed the adventure of exile and the old people's home, hearing the hope in Mother's voice made her realize how much she'd like to go home.

Pulling the onyx cigarette holder from his lips, Frosell shook his head. "I'm afraid not, Marie," he said. "Nordling says it is still not safe for me—*us*—to return to Paris; they're still looking for scapegoats to persecute." He pointed with disdain at the letter he'd thrown to the floor.

Marie's face fell. "So, where do we go, Oscar? Where *is* safe for us?" She glanced over at where Heddy was hiding, as if she knew by instinct precisely where her daughter was.

"I have an associate in Boulogne," Frosell said. "He has a place in . . ." He eyed Nordling's driver with suspicion. "I think you ought to take your leave now, young man." His voice was firm, cold.

The driver tipped his cap and made a hasty exit, taking great care to ease the heavy front door gently closed behind him.

Heddy watched the young driver climb into the shiny black car that awaited him on the gravel driveway. In a heartbeat, he disappeared down toward the narrow winding road beyond the rusted iron gates at the end. The little girl's heart weighed heavy in her chest as she studied her parents' concerned expressions; she really didn't want to have to uproot and move again, especially not so soon.

"There's a place in Saint-Cloud," Frosell said as soon as the driver was out of earshot. "Philippe promised we could rent it for as long as we need to." He offered his wife a reassuring smile, and his eyes twinkled with warmth. "It's a villa, and it'll be far better for us than this old place." As he spoke softly, Frosell gazed around at the peeling wallpaper and warped floorboards. "Especially if it looks like we won't be able to return to Paris anytime soon."

Marie returned the smile, although her eyes belied her worry. "I suppose this was only ever meant to be temporary," she said.

"Precisely," Frosell replied. "And I think our daughter will take to villa life just fine—isn't that right, Heddy?"

Heddy crept out from the hiding place that had not hidden her too well. "Yes, Father," she said with a sheepish grin.

"I guess we'd best pack up our things again," Marie said. "Do you need any help, Heddy?"

The little girl shook her head. "No, thank you, Mother. I can manage," she replied with her customary politeness. The truth was, she hadn't entirely unpacked.

Frosell made a few hasty telephone calls to his business acquaintance, Philippe Lacoste, while Marie and Heddy gathered up the meager belongings they'd brought with them to the Montmartre retirement home only a few short weeks ago. Together, and in silence, they packed them into the car. "It's all settled," Frosell informed his family as he lit the last of his penultimate pack of cigarettes by means of celebration. "We may rent the villa in Saint-Cloud until it is safe for us to return to Paris."

With that, Oscar Frosell ushered his wife and daughter from the old people's home and into the car; it had been fewer than three hours since Nordling's driver had delivered the general consul's letter.

As if reflecting Frosell's mood, the sky clouded over with corpulent gray clouds—the type that threaten heavy rain yet fail to deliver. Absently, he clenched his teeth as he drove along the narrow lanes leading away from Montmartre and out into the French countryside.

The trip itself was a little over thirty-one kilometers and would normally have taken a little over an hour, but Frosell was forced to keep his speed down to avoid the myriad holes dotting the roads—the majority of which were the legacy of mortar rounds and stray carpet bombs.

"Are we there yet?" Heddy asked, somewhat inevitably, from her mother's knee.

Marie smiled at her daughter. "Almost," she gave her rote reply, even though she knew that Heddy knew they were far from their destination and the child just wanted to speak. "Are you looking forward to living in a villa, Heddy?"

The little girl shrugged. "I guess."

"It has a yard," Marie persisted.

Heddy gave her mother the reassuring smile she knew she was looking for. She was disappointed to be leaving Montmartre for anywhere other than Paris, as she really wasn't relishing the second upheaval in as many months. And besides, the abandoned old people's home had *grounds*, which were far better than a mere yard!

A dull rumbling sound filled the car, like the grumble of distant thunder. Frosell eased up on the gas and allowed the Berliet to coast a little. He stared straight ahead through the windshield and muttered something quite unseemly beneath his breath.

"Oh, my," Marie exclaimed as she turned back around to see the mammoth gray truck looming ahead. "Is that . . . ?"

Frosell nodded. "Germans," was all he had to say.

He'd read about the scattered pockets of German resistance. They had dispersed through the French countryside once the Allies stormed the northern beaches and began fighting their way inland. Although many of the occupying forces had simply returned to the homeland or surrendered, a hard core remained who refused to believe the Third Reich could ever be defeated; Frosell wondered if they were determined to fight all the way down to their last bullet. With a sinking sensation in his stomach, Frosell eased the car onto the overgrown grass verge to give the German truck enough space to pass.

Heddy pressed her face up against the car's window as the truck lumbered by. She grinned and waved at the ragtag assortment of German soldiers who sat in the back; they were all hunkered down beneath the green flapping canvas, and each one clutched their gun as if it were some favorite toy.

A couple of the soldiers waved at the little girl in the expensive black car, although it was almost too dark to see its occupants. A few of them called out something in their native language, which Heddy didn't understand. She guessed they were just being friendly, though; for all the distinctly unpleasant things she'd heard about the Germans, seeing them this close took away much of the fear their reputation garnered. They looked to be regular people to her, albeit dirty, tired, and miserable.

Heddy jumped as a sudden noise filled the air. Away in the distance flashed a bright white light, which accompanied the dull, muffled bang. Illuminated by the phosphorescent glow, Heddy saw a truck—bigger than the one they'd just passed but so far away as to appear no more than an inch long—fly high up into the air.

Acting purely through instinct, Frosell pressed down on the accelerator, veered the car from the verge, and sped off down the road; most likely the truck had hit a mine—the more remote country roads were littered with them—or encountered unexploded ordnance.

The remainder of the trip to Saint-Cloud was made in silence. Frosell drove as quickly as he dared, eyes fixed firmly on the road ahead, and Marie worried about what her daughter had just witnessed. She hoped against hope Heddy was far too young to fully comprehend the inevitable deaths of the poor soldiers in the distant truck and she wouldn't carry the trauma around for the rest of her life.

Heddy watched the column of thick, black smoke as it spiraled up from the burning truck and high into the sky. In her imagination, it was a huge flock of countless tiny black birds rising up toward the bloated old clouds as they prepared to fly south to sunnier climes for the winter.

"I don't believe it," Frosell broke the silence as he pulled the Berliet into the driveway leading up to the villa. He slowed the car almost to a stop and peered through the window.

"Oh my word," Marie gasped, her hand to her mouth, eyes wide and staring.

"What *is* that, Father?" Heddy chirped from behind, quite fascinated by the huge metal object—it was almost as long as the truck they'd passed earlier—which had ploughed up a goodly amount of the villa's immaculately tended front lawn.

Even though she had spent the entirety of her young life in wartime, Heddy Frosell had never before seen an unexploded V2 rocket.

CHAPTER SIX

Porte Dauphine Commissariat de Police, Paris.
September 16ᵗʰ, 1944.

At around the same time as Oscar Frosell and his family found themselves confronted by unexploded German ordnance on the front lawn of their new Saint-Cloud home, Admiral and Madame Dumesnil were making themselves comfortable in the office of Police Commissioner Richeaux.

"Thank you for making the time to meet with us," Madame Dumesnil said as she smoothed her silk dress beneath her trim derrière before taking her seat.

The police commissioner grunted a little. "I do not usually receive visitors without an invitation, madame." He was doing his best to remain as polite as his hectic schedule would allow. "But I am happy to make an exception for such distinguished company." He smiled at the admiral, who sat in the cheap metal chair next to his good lady wife.

Admiral Dumesnil was wearing his full naval regalia, of course, as he was keen to impress Richeaux; the strategy had clearly worked like a charm, as he and Madame Dumesnil had been ushered directly into the commissioner's office. He took off his hat and rested it upon his knee in an attempt to appear a tad more informal.

"We are here about the vacant apartment at 6 Rue Dufrenoy," the admiral began. "It was abandoned several weeks ago."

The commissioner nodded. "I am aware of that address," he said. "Several of my agents were involved in an arrest there."

"Then you will know it is the former address of a traitor," Madame Dumesnil added. "He and his family fled when they knew they were about to be exposed as collaborators and arrested."

The admiral leaned forward, his voice in a hushed, conspiratorial tone. "It is far worse than that, Commissioner Richeaux—may I call you *Commissioner*?" His eyes darted about the room, as if he feared someone might be listening in.

The commissioner nodded; he really didn't care too much what the odious little man in the uniform called him as long as he said what he'd come to say and got the hell out of his office.

"Monsieur Frosell is more than merely a *collaborateur*, he is a German citizen—a fact he has managed to keep well hidden, until now." Dumesnil's seat squeaked as he sat back, his eyes fixed on the commissioner's.

"And I understand he's a Gestapo agent, to boot," Madame Dumesnil chipped in. She furrowed her brow and lowered her eyes to show how incredibly upset she was by the whole affair.

Commissioner Richeaux leaned forward, bridged his fingers, and rested his elbows on his paper-strewn desk. "Admiral, Madame Dumesnil, as you can see, I am very busy. Since Vichy fell, I have been inundated almost daily with accusations of collaboration and collusion aimed at Parisians—be they French citizens or otherwise." He tapped a finger on a thick pile of paperwork that clung precariously to the edge of his desk. "I also have *real* crimes to deal with. Did you know there have been almost four times the number of burglaries since the occupying forces were routed? Common assault has tripled, and murder is twice what it was before." He paused for effect, studying the well-to-do faces of the admiral and his wife, who sat expectantly across his desk. "I have little time for unfounded accusations and hearsay, I'm afraid."

"We are not here to make accusations," Dumesnil said. "The truth about Oscar Frosell will be out all in good time. There is documentation available that clearly shows his collusion. And I'm sure a quick call to the consulate he claims as his own will clear up the matter of his nationality."

"So, why *are* you here?" The commissioner showed his impatience; the pompous admiral and his wife were not taking the hint at all.

"We are here," Admiral Dumesnil told him, "to inform you we will be taking over the Frosell apartment at Rue Dufrenoy on behalf of Commandante Alla Dumesnil, the esteemed major in the women's section of the French Revolutionary Air Force." The admiral paused to catch his breath, no doubt for dramatic effect. "We are asking for the support of the police force in this matter."

"Excuse me?" Commissioner Richeaux eased himself back in his chair, his brow furrowed in a deep frown; he was having difficulty believing what he'd just heard.

"The commandante is very highly thought of within the French Air Force, and by General de Gaulle himself," Madame Dumesnil added.

The commissioner studied the admiral and his wife. Clearly, the full naval regalia—medal ribbons and all—were meant to either impress or intimidate him. Unfortunately for the Dumesnils, the commissioner had become so used to dealing with all ranks of the military during the months following the Allied invasion that the admiral's uniform performed neither function. "I'm sorry, Admiral, Madame Dumesnil," he said with a firm voice. "You can't simply claim property like this—no matter who you are representing."

"Commissioner Richeaux," Admiral Dumesnil persisted, "we have a letter . . ." He fumbled around in his pocket to produce a folded sheet of paper, much as a street magician might conjure an astounded onlooker's chosen playing card. "It's a requisition order," he explained as he carefully unfolded it and began to read. "I commandeer herewith the living quarters situated on the second floor in 6 Rue Dufrenoy, which have been left by Monsieur Frosell, *Gestapo agent . . .*" Dumesnil enunciated the words as if with great relish. "I commandeer also all furniture, linen, and household equipment to be found therein. An inventory of such things shall be compiled by some competent person appointed for such." He lay the paper down on the commissioner's desk with a smug smile.

"It's signed by General Bouscat," Madame Dumesnil added. "He's a general in the air force."

Commissioner Richeaux sighed. He knew full well who General Bouscat was, although as to precisely what jurisdiction he had to be requisitioning private homes in freed Paris was a tad beyond him. "There are special authorities and channels to go through, paperwork to be presented." The commissioner refused to waver in his duty to protect the property, much to the admiral's chagrin. "And, of course, investigations to be completed," he explained. "I appreciate we are living in times of great change and upheaval—some might even say they are anarchic—but French law *must* be observed and adhered to."

Madame Dumesnil cast a sideways glance at her husband. "The commandante will not be happy to hear of your obstinacy, Commissioner," she said.

"I am quite sure Commandante *Dumesnil* will understand the need to abide by the law of the land, having fought so bravely to protect it," the commissioner said with a wry smile. "Now, if you will excuse me, I have a lot of work to catch up on."

The admiral opened his mouth to speak but decided against it. The police commissioner was already leafing through a yellowing sheaf of rough handwritten notes—an obvious indication that the meeting was well and truly over. He stood and placed his hat firmly on top of his head. "Thank you for your time, Commissioner." His tone was quite civil. "You have been most helpful."

The commissioner lifted his eyes from the paperwork as the Dumesnils made their way out of his small office. "You are most welcome," he said to the back of their heads. As he watched the two of them walk briskly along the hallway to the commissariat's front door, he picked up the phone and dialed an internal number.

Something in the look between Madame Dumesnil and her officious husband hadn't sat quite right with the commissioner. Over twenty years in the police force had taught him well to read people, and he had a gut feeling something was much amiss with the Dumesnils. "Henri?" he said, the moment the phone was picked up, "I'd like you to pay a visit to 6 Rue Dufrenoy; take a couple of officers with you." He listened to his inspector's reply. "That's the one. I think it's worth checking out, though, just to make sure everything is as it should be."

With a heavy sigh, the commissioner rested the receiver back on its cradle and eyed the mountains of paperwork covering every square inch of his desk. The last thing he needed was Admiral Dumesnil and his daughter stirring up trouble—war heroes or not.

6 Rue Dufrenoy, Paris. September 16th, 1944.

Inspector Henri Pinson and his officers were greeted outside the Rue Dufrenoy apartment by an irate Georges Hallier, who was standing by the main doors.

"They have no right to be in here!" Hallier shouted across at them, even before they'd had the chance to get out of the police car.

"Good afternoon, monsieur." Pinson sought to disarm the elderly man's fury with a warm smile. "How may I be of help?"

"You're not the Seine Police," the old man said rudely, quite obviously put out by the inspector's presence. "I called the Seine Police!"

Pinson took a deep breath before addressing the man once more. "We're from the Commissariat de Police; the commissioner asked us to check on number six. I'm sure we can help you, nonetheless." He gave the old man another smile.

The mention of the apartment number calmed Hallier down a tad, although his bestubbled cheeks were still puffed up and flushed bright crimson. "I am the landlord," he explained, "and I have informed those . . . people that they cannot be in the apartment."

"Which apartment, monsieur?" Pinson asked, although he had more than an inkling as to the landlord's reply.

"Monsieur Frosell's."

"I think we should take a look." Pinson reached around Hallier, pushed open the doors, and stepped into the grand vestibule. "If you'd be so kind as to lead the way . . ."

The landlord ushered the three agents to the small elevator, which they took to the second floor. There, he herded them to the front door of the Frosells' apartment. He stooped down to pluck a crumpled sheet of paper from the floor, groaning loudly with the exertion. "It was sealed by the Swedish Consul when the Frosells left for their . . . vacation." Hallier waved the paper beneath Pinson's nose. "See? They have no rights to be in there!"

Pinson rapped on the door.

"Who is it?"

"It is the police, mademoiselle," the inspector replied. "Could you open the door?" There came the sounds of chains rattling and locks clicking, and eventually, the heavy door swung open.

"Can I help you?" Alla Dumesnil asked curtly. "My friends and I were just sitting down to dinner."

Pinson peered around the young woman, to be hailed by waves and friendly smiles from another two young women who stood at the far end of the expansive atrium. "And you are . . . ?"

The young woman held out a hand for him to shake. "Alla Dumesnil—*Commandante* Alla Dumesnil, French Air Force." Her handshake was formal and incredibly firm.

"You're not supposed to be in here!" Hallier pushed by Pinson and into the apartment. "You are all illegal!" He waved the sheet of paper around like it was a magical amulet designed purely for the exorcism of unwanted young ladies. "You must all leave—*now!*"

Pinson followed the landlord inside the apartment. He'd heard the stories about the opulence of the place but had thought them exaggerations. Upon seeing the wealth on display there, Pinson found that, if anything, the reports had been underplayed. It also made a refreshing change to see a place such as this appear to be untouched; so many he'd seen since the general strike had been trashed and looted in the name of liberation. "I apologize, mademoiselle, but if you are not entitled to be in here, then I must ask you to leave."

Alla stood her ground, hands on hips in defiance. "I will not leave. I am a French citizen, and I have a right to claim the property of a *collaborateur*, Gestapo agent, and enemy of the people!"

"If you have the appropriate paperwork—that would certainly help clear things up," Pinson told her. "If you'd be so kind as to show it to me, I shall be on my way, and you good people may get back to your dinner."

"She has no paperwork!" Hallier snapped. "She has broken the seal and entered Monsieur Frosell's home illegally!"

Alla shot the old man a withering glance. "Do you not know who I am?" she spat. "I am Commandante Alla Dumesnil. My father is Admiral Dumesnil." She puffed out her chest and stared the landlord down.

"I'm afraid it doesn't matter who you or your father are, mademoiselle," Pinson explained in a calm, succinct tone. "Unless you have legal documentation stating your rights to occupy this property, you will have to leave."

"This is an outrage!" Alla shouted. "You give preference to a German and *war criminal* over a hero of the resistance?" She stormed away from Pinson and his officers, her flared temper even causing Hallier to shrink back. "*We are going nowhere, monsieur!*" she screamed over her shoulder.

Even though he didn't particularly need backup, Pinson was at least a little relieved when a pair of officers from the Seine Police finally made an appearance. He commandeered them to assist in removing Alla and her two friends, although the latter were happy to leave without too much of a fuss.

"My father will hear of this!" Alla yelled in Pinson's face as he and two officers escorted her from the apartment. "Get your hands off me!" Her voice resounded about the high ceilings as she struggled against the police, all which made for a strange echo of savagery among the lavish surroundings.

Once the commandante was clear of the door, Hallier and the Seine Police officers replaced the seal and locked it. "I will have my locksmith fit extra locks," the landlord said. "They will not get in again."

Pinson escorted the commandante out into the street and ensured she was clear of the main doors to number 6 before having his officers let her go; as tempting as the thought was to make an example of the entitled young lady, the inspector's sense of self-preservation held him back from arresting her. "You are free to go, Commandante," he told her.

Alla took a step toward the apartment building, as if taunting Pinson. "I have an apartment here," she told him, "or are you going to prevent me from going in there too?" she sneered.

Pinson shook his head. "No, mademoiselle, I am not. Although, I must caution you against attempting to return to the Frosell apartment. If you do, you *will* be arrested."

"Arrested?" Alla shouted for the benefit of the street's residents, who were hiding behind twitching curtains. "You would arrest me?" She snorted her derision at Pinson. "Just who the hell do you think you are? I'll have your job for this, *Inspector.*" She spat the word like it was a bad taste in her mouth. "General de Gaulle will hear of this!"

Pinson watched as the commandante stormed off like some spoiled brat turned away from a birthday party and couldn't help but wonder how she'd managed to become a hero.

Offices of the Provisional Government of the French Republic, Paris. September 16th, 1944.

Captain Girardot knocked gently upon the door, a single sheet of white paper clutched in one hand.

"Come!" a harsh voice barked from within.

The general's adjutant eased open the door and stepped inside the long, dimly lit room with his heart thumping heavily.

Charles de Gaulle waved Girardot in with an exasperated huff. "This had better be important. Can you not see I'm busy?" he chastised the young man with an apologetic glance at the half dozen dignitaries with whom he shared the wide oak meeting table—none of whom Girardot recognized.

The adjutant swallowed hard. It was never easy interrupting de Gaulle's meetings—the man's fearsome reputation was certainly well earned. Girardot made his way across the room and whispered quietly in de Gaulle's ear. He then placed the paper upon the table and took a step back.

"What is this?" de Gaulle exclaimed, his eyes flitting across the page. He snatched the paper up from the desk and read it through once again.

"It's a requisition order," Girardot replied, his voice so timid as to be barely perceptible. "For the Rue Dufrenoy apartment."

"I can see that!" de Gaulle was incensed. "This was supposed to have been taken care of weeks ago. I spoke with Monsieur Luizet personally!" he barked. "If the prefect of the Seine Police himself can't undertake such a simple task, then perhaps we should look to replace him?"

"I understand it's still under letters of protection and diplomatic immunity of the Swedish General Consulate," Girardot offered.

Angry, de Gaulle snatched his pen up from the table and scribbled his signature across the bottom of the order. "Let this be an end to the whole farce! And you get word to Police Commissioner Richeaux at Porte Dauphine that he is best advised not to take the side of a known collaborator and traitor against me—or the next order I'll be signing will be for his execution!"

With that, de Gaulle dismissed the aide with a wave of his hand and returned to discussing more urgent matters of state.

CHAPTER SEVEN

Rue Dufrenoy, Paris. September 17ᵗʰ, 1944.

The squealing of tires and revving of engines broke the tranquil dawn chorus. A handful of police cars swung into the street, drawing puzzled glances from Jacques and Madeleine Artois as they set up the small array of tables and chairs outside their café. As they looked on in amazement, the police cars, followed by a half dozen black vans, screeched to a halt outside number 6.

Curtains twitched and front doors cracked open all along Rue Dufrenoy as inquisitive residents strained to see what further drama was befalling the Frosells' second-floor apartment; there was little sympathy for the family now, as the vicious rumors regarding Monsieur Frosell's treachery against his adopted country had spread like wildfires.

Inspector Henri Pinson gave out a heavy sigh, his breath forming tiny plumes of white in the early autumn air. This was not how he'd intended to spend his day, nor had he ever considered his role as police inspector to be tantamount to authorized looting. Still, he had his orders from Commissioner Richeaux, who had received *his*

78

orders from somewhere way above his authority. Pinson had heard rumors going around the commissariat that the commissioner had been on the receiving end of a serious dressing down from high up in the ranks—some had even ventured from de Gaulle himself—and more than just his job had been laid firmly on the line.

"Let's do this with as little drama as possible," Pinson said to the policemen as they got out of their vehicles and surrounded him. He sighed again; there was little hope of that, since the dramatic appearance and entirely unnecessary tire squealing had alerted everyone in the street to their presence. Already a small crowd of nosy neighbors had gathered a safe distance behind the black vans. "You know what we came to do, so let's get it done with decorum and respect—"

"I'll take it from here, Inspector Pinson," a tall, gray-skinned man interrupted. He threw down his spent cigarette butt and ground it into the road as he slammed the door of his van behind him; the harsh, tinny noise resounded between the tall, majestic buildings of Rue Dufrenoy like a rifle shot. Smoothing down the dark gray suit, which was a perfect match to his sallow features, the man gave a nod to the occupants of the other, perfectly identical vehicles parked up in a neat convoy stretching a good way down along the street.

Taken aback by the sudden interjection, Pinson eyed the man with suspicion. The commissioner had informed him there would be outside involvement at Rue Dufrenoy, although he had not specified exactly who would be accompanying the police that morning, nor had he divulged any names. By the expensive cut of the tall man's suit, Pinson could only assume he was government of some description—although in those tumultuous days, it was sometimes difficult to figure out precisely what that meant.

"Take as much as you can," the tall man ordered his—and Pinson's—men. "You know what to prioritize." This he directed at his own team of a dozen or so black-clad men, who seemed to Pinson to be ex-military types; he also noted they all appeared to be carrying badly concealed guns.

"I have my orders . . . ," Pinson protested.

"As do I—and mine supersede yours, *Inspector* Pinson." The tall man's tone carried a professional curtness clearly intended to put Pinson firmly in his place. He waved a hand at his team, and they filed into the apartment building and headed up the stairs to the second floor in one fluid motion.

Pinson and his policemen followed on, keeping a respectful distance as the door to the Frosell apartment was unsealed and smashed open.

Aided by the police, the black-suited men swarmed through the apartment. They plucked valuable artwork from the walls, gathered together ornaments, statuettes, and vases, all to be unceremoniously stacked on the pavement directly outside the apartment building. There were multitudes of exquisitely detailed Sèvres and Limoges porcelain figurines; statues crafted in bronze, gold, and ivory from China and Japan; along with more than forty signed paintings by Raphael, Anthony van Dyck, Degas, and Watteau; and Bokhara carpets—which were all museum pieces, along with the fine antique

furniture. The officials also removed over a hundred carats in dia-
monds and innumerable crystals, gems, and semiprecious stones.

Pinson wandered between the myriad rooms in the spacious
apartment, his heart sinking at every priceless item carted away by
the tall man's people and his own men. They were just following
orders, he knew that, but did they have to go about it like a swarm
of ravenous locusts?

A commotion came from the far end of the hallway—raised voices
and what sounded like a dog barking. Pinson quickened his step and
made his way over.

"It tried to bite me!" one of Pinson's officers moaned. He held a
small pink rocking chair between himself and the angry German
shepherd, who stood on the lace-covered child's bed with its hackles
raised and teeth bared. "Somebody shoot it!" the officer shouted, his
voice trembling with fear.

Younker snarled at the policeman, determined to protect Heddy's
room even though the little girl was no longer there. He'd been fed
and watered by Alla Dumesnil and her friends, and had even learned
to accept them, but now he was confronted by a horde of strangers
who were systematically taking his home apart. He jumped from the
bed and ran toward the officer wielding the chair.

A single shot rang out, startling the dog, the police, and Inspector
Pinson.

Pinson stepped back as Younker sprinted out of Heddy's bedroom
and off down the hallway, tail between his legs. "Hold your fire!"
Pinson snapped at the trigger-happy agent to his left. The last thing he

needed that morning was to have to fill out the paperwork explaining
how someone got shot on his watch.

The man simply stared at Pinson, his gun still pointed toward the
retreating dog. A tiny wisp of white smoke curled from the Beretta as
the air outside the child's room filled with the acrid stink of gunpowder.

"Stand down." The tall man appeared as if from nowhere. He smiled
at Pinson as his man holstered his gun and went about the business
of ransacking Oscar Frosell's home.

"We're ready, sir." Another of the agents sidled up to the tall man,
his voice low. "Just waiting on your order . . ."

"I'll be right there," the tall man told him. "We're almost done," he
said to Pinson. "We'll be out of your hair within the hour." With that,
he turned on his heels and made his way over to the master bedroom.

Pinson followed and arrived at the Frosells' bedroom in time to
see three of the black-suited men standing around the twin safes
with their arms folded across their chests. Molded against one of the
safe's hinges were finger-thick strips of what Pinson recognized as
Composition C-4, the stable explosive the British had brought along
with them after Normandy.

He also saw that, with ruthless efficiency, the room had been
completely stripped of anything immediately portable. Where
expensive paintings had hung on the immaculately papered walls
were now only faint outlines, which looked like sad, clinging ghosts.
And where antique ornaments had adorned shelves, Victorian display
cases, and the huge marble fireplace, only clear spaces in the thick,
settled dust remained. Pinson also noted the bedside rug had been

removed; the elegant canopy bed had been shoved aside in haste, leaving a pair of deep scratches in the polished wood floor. The rug itself—genuine sixteenth-century Persian—was rolled up in the hallway outside the bedroom, all ready to be hauled away to the awaiting vans by the black-suited looters.

"Wait just a minute." The inspector caught the tall man's arm. "You can't do this. My orders are to—"

The tall man snorted and pulled his arm away from Pinson's grasp. "I really don't care what *your* orders are, Inspector Pinson," he growled. Across the room, his agents were busy fiddling with detonators, adjusting them just so in the C-4. "We have a job to do here."

Pinson shook his head. "This isn't right; I'm going to call the commissioner." He knew in his heart the threat carried no weight with the tall man, but felt nonetheless as if he had to do *something*. After all, Oscar Frosell was not only protected by the Swedish consulate, he'd not been found guilty of anything.

"Why don't you do that?" the tall man replied with a wry grin. "In the meantime, you may wish to take a step or two back." He nodded toward the men in the room. They had strung a triumvirate of thin wires from the detonators to a portable battery pack and retreated with it to the safety of the *en suite* bathroom.

"All clear!" a deep, resonant voice called out.

The tall man stepped out of the doorway and into the hall, ushering Pinson to one side as he did so. "Clear!" he shouted his reply.

A dull, muffled *whoomp* filled the apartment, along with a nauseating, acrid chemical smell. A thick plume of smoke and dust billowed out from the Frosells' bedroom and floated out along the hallway.

"Oh my . . . ," the deep voice exclaimed through fits of coughing.

Pinson followed the tall man back into the bedroom, to be met by the sight of what remained of Oscar Frosell's safe.

The door had been blown completely off its hinges; it lay twisted and all but unrecognizable at the foot of the bed—the tall man's agents had done a precise job; this was quite clearly not their first time relieving a safe of its valuable contents. The thick motes of dust stirred up by the explosion settled slowly about the room, accompanied by small shreds of paper that flittered and danced in wildly swirling eddies created by the bustling agents. Upon close inspection, Pinson could see the scraps of colored paper were, in fact, stamps—each one quite old and no doubt incredibly valuable.

But it wasn't the stamps, bonds, land registry documents, or mortgage papers that interested the tall man—it was the pile of gold and platinum ingots stacked neatly inside the thick walls of Frosell's safe, along with the innumerable precious gems.

The breath caught in Pinson's throat as he studied the stacks of ingots. Of course, he could have little idea as to their precise value, although he guessed they were most likely worth far more even than the art, antique furniture, and eclectic collection of antiquities, which had been so unceremoniously carried from Frosell's apartment. Surely they couldn't just do this; there had to be due process before even the French government could sequester private property—even that of an accused *collaborateur*?

Pinson turned his back on the ransacked bedroom and made his way out of the apartment, rounding up his officers as he went; he didn't want them to have any further part of this travesty. He felt sick to his stomach and ashamed to his very core at having been part of such an almighty injustice; it made him embarrassed to be French.

Out on the street, the tall man's small army of agents was busy lugging works of art, furniture, jewelry, rugs, and tapestries down the stairs and into the fleet of black vans. There were even dark-suited men lugging baby clothes and children's toys along the street and hurling them through the gaping doors of the penultimate van; and not one of them showed the slightest iota of remorse or shame.

The neighborhood was out in force. A considerable crowd had gathered, all overcome with curiosity, huddled around to watch as the drama unfolded. It reminded Pinson too much of the aftermath of the strategic Allied bombing raids on Saint-Nazaire back in '42—he'd been stationed there before being seconded to Paris. There, the survivors would venture from their homes the moment the dust had settled—and often while they could still hear the dull thrum of the bombers' engines—to ogle and pick through the ruined houses and belongings of their less fortunate neighbors. He saw the same covetous envy in the eyes of the Rue Dufrenoy residents that morning, and among them, his eyes met with those of Commandante Dumesnil.

Alla Dumesnil gave the inspector a cursory nod and a smirk, which made him cringe. He knew somehow she and her corrupt family would be at the bottom of all this, which was why they had been ordered to leave enough furniture in the apartment for her to continue living there. Even so, she looked pissed they were removing any of it. Sadly, he also knew there would be nothing he or the commissioner could do about it.

Pinson climbed into his car, gunned the engine, and eased his way through the gathered neighbors. On the opposite side of the street stood the Frosells' dog, tail between its legs and a forlorn expression on its handsome face. As Pinson drove away from the shameful scene at Rue Dufrenoy, one of the tall man's agents threw chunks of brick at the poor thing until it ran away.

CHAPTER EIGHT

The Swedish Consulate, Paris. October 1944.

"This is getting most tiresome," General Consul Nordling grumbled beneath his breath. He shuffled around on his tired, creaking chair and eyed with disdain the stocky man who sat opposite him. The consul had always held a healthy regard of the Second Bureau and its agents—the infamous French Secret Service—but Agent Avot was beginning to test that more than a little. "I have things to do, Lieutenant Avot. I'm a very busy man these days, what with everything that's going on in Paris."

The Secret Service agent eased back in the old wooden chair and folded his hands in his lap. He and General Consul Nordling weren't exactly what he'd consider to be great friends—they'd had lively conversations at the admiral's parties from time to time, plus a handful of meetings at the consulate—but it still irked him when the man played the officious card. He knew all too well what Nordling was referring to, and had no time for the man's blatant self-aggrandizing. "Raoul, my friend, you know I wouldn't be here if it weren't entirely necessary." Avot couldn't help but glance around Nordling's somewhat stark, spartan office—he'd always thought someone of such standing would warrant more salubrious surroundings. Perhaps that came with a position at the actual embassy, or it could have been simply that the Swedes were a particularly frugal nation.

"I suppose that is true," Nordling replied with a heavy sigh. He'd planned to spend his day working on his own pet project, namely continuing to build himself up as the Man Who Saved Paris and preparing for the fame he could practically hear calling him. He was already a good third of the way through writing his extensive memoirs and had big ideas about approaching a literary agent he knew to represent him in Hollywood—a moving picture based on his life, with the pivotal moment being his persuading von Choltitz not to decimate Paris, would be a most fitting climax of the piece. Nordling had even gone so far as to pick out Cary Grant as the actor to play his part—or perhaps even Gary Cooper.

So, the last thing he wanted was to have to deal with Jean Edmund Avot of the *Arme Blindée Cavalerie*, especially given the delicate subject of the lieutenant's visit that morning.

"Raoul, how well do you know Oscar Frosell?" Avot asked Nordling for the second time. From the tone in his voice and the over-familiar use of the consul's first name, it was clear his patience was wearing thin; he had no more desire to be in Nordling's office discussing Frosell than did the Swedish general consul.

"I barely know the man," Nordling replied with honesty. "I met with him for the first—and only—time a month or so ago. I suggested somewhere he could go to be safe from persecution."

"You *assisted* him fleeing the city?" Avot sat forward in his chair and fixed Nordling with an accusatory glare. "A suspected Gestapo agent and Nazi collaborator?"

Nordling felt his cheeks flush and wondered why suddenly he felt as if *he* were in the spotlight; exactly who was the alleged traitor here? "I merely suggested he and his family might be safer at the old folks' home for a while," he explained, "on the advice of a mutual friend."

"And that would be Admiral Dumesnil?"

Nordling nodded. Already he was regretting ever having agreed to get involved with Dumesnils' wealthy friend. Monsieur Frosell was proving to be far more trouble than he was worth. "He was concerned about the Frosells' safety following the accusations and the scrutiny of de Gaulle's people," he told Avot. "I did what I could to help, that's all."

Avot studied the general consul's rotund, pallid face. Something about the way the corner of the man's left eye twitched as he spoke told Avot he was making Nordling nervous. Either that or the man had something to hide.

"So," Avot continued, his eyes fixed firmly on Nordling's, "you aided and abetted a suspected collaborator? You were well aware of the accusations being aimed at Oscar Frosell, and yet still you warned him to leave the city . . . *and* you gave him a place to go?"

Nordling's left eye twitched a little more.

"Lieutenant, you have to understand—they were only *accusations.*" Nordling struggled to keep his voice steady. Despite his standing as a respected and experienced diplomat, the one thing he hated was to be put on the spot like this. "And the man has a family."

"They are *serious* accusations, Raoul." Avot leaned farther forward in his chair, as if to further emphasize the gravitas of his words. "We are not just talking some minor misdemeanor or malicious gossip here. Surely you understand that?" He let out a long, heavy sigh. "You know Monsieur Frosell is not only a suspected *collaborateur* and profiteer, but also a member of the Gestapo." He watched with some amusement as Nordling's eye twitched some more. "I'm sure you can see the position this places you in—along with the entire Swedish Consul, of course?"

As Nordling slumped in his seat, the cold metal of its tired old frame groaned beneath his weight. His mind raced as he contemplated the full weight of Avot's words, and he felt his heroic standing as the savior of Paris and national hero eroding with each passing moment. He cursed Dumesnil and that pushy, overbearing wife of his—*and* their damn daughter who had ideas way above her station simply because she was connected to de Gaulle by her sycophant fiancé. Nordling was quickly beginning to rue the day he'd ever set eyes on Admiral Dumesnil. Moreover, he was angry at having been put in the awkward position of facilitating the requisition of Frosell's property and valuables by denying the man's citizenship—even though General de Gaulle himself had ultimately become involved. That, in a way, Nordling considered to have vindicated his actions. Above all, though, Nordling felt embarrassed he'd allowed himself to be manipulated by the Dumesnils into allowing a fellow countryman and his family—they had a young child, for God's sake!—to be driven from their home and hunted down like a pack of wild animals. All in all, Raoul Nordling was beginning to understand how Judas must have felt upon receiving his seven pieces of ill-gotten silver.

"You do know this is going to go further, General Consul Nordling?" Avot pressed. "Oscar Frosell—a Swedish citizen—stands accused of some exceptionally serious war crimes, and that is only ever going to reflect badly upon the Swedish consulate . . . and yourself, of course. Do you realize the possible implications for you of assisting a Nazi collaborator and Gestapo agent—especially in de Gaulle's freed Paris?"

Nordling grunted at the lieutenant; a sick, sinking feeling was settling in the pit of his stomach as he felt his fame, fortune, and dreams of watching Cary Grant playing himself up on the silver screen evaporating before his very eyes. He fidgeted in his chair and fiddled with one of the expensive fountain pens—a gift from Winston Churchill, as it happened—on the desk in front of him. He thought carefully for a moment, his brow furrowed, eyes squinting.

"But what if Oscar Frosell was not actually a Swedish citizen, though?" He spoke quietly, as if the words were struggling to get out. "How would that change matters, Lieutenant Avot?"

Avot fiddled with his tie and shifted in his chair; it was his turn to feel the unease permeating the dull, gray office. "What are you trying to tell me, General Consul Nordling?" He knew the answer, naturally; he was not a stupid man.

"Oscar Frosell was born in Canada," Nordling offered. "His father was Canadian." Of course, he'd deliberately neglected to add the fact that Carl Frosell had been Swedish through and through. He straightened up against the back of his chair and looked the lieutenant directly in the eye. "His mother, the countess Artemis da Ponte, was Italian."

"Are you telling me, General Consul Nordling, Monsieur Oscar Frosell is *not* a Swedish citizen?"

Nordling nodded. Lying by omission was still lying, his conscience screamed at him, but he was now in full self-preservation mode. "What I'm telling you, Lieutenant Avot, is that Oscar Frosell is German. I only helped him because he's a friend of a friend, not because of his nationality."

"And you can prove this?" If Avot was skeptical about Nordling's new claim, he wasn't showing it.

"I can have the paperwork put together if necessary," Nordling replied. "Along with documented proof of Frosell's association with the *Comptoir National d'Achats et de Distribution*." The general consul paused for effect before giving out a loud snort. "While it doesn't prove he was Gestapo, it does show, beyond all doubt, Oscar Frosell worked with the occupying forces in France to aid their war effort."

Avot contemplated this awhile; this sudden—and wholly un-expected—change of gear had actually nonplussed him a little. "This changes everything, of course." He finally broke the silence. "Especially for you, Raoul."

Nordling gave the lieutenant a weak smile. "I suppose it does," he agreed quietly. "So, as you can see, Lieutenant Avot, the matter of Oscar Frosell and his alleged treachery against the people of France has little to do with Sweden."

"And you will be prepared to put your name to this?" Avot watched as Nordling's eye twitched a little. "Testify in court, even, if necessary?"

"I will gather the relevant paperwork together for you, Lieutenant," Nordling offered by means of a reply. "Now, if you would be so kind as to excuse me, I do have a lot of work to do."

Taking this as his cue, Avot struggled from his seat and stood over Nordling's desk. "Thank you for your time, General Consul," he said with forced politeness. "You have been most helpful." He turned to leave as Nordling began shuffling random papers about on his cluttered desk. "I will be sure to keep you up to date as to how my investigations into Monsieur Frosell go."

Nordling dismissed Avot with a wave of his hand. "There's no need to involve the consulate any further on that, Lieutenant Avot," he said. "We are here to take care of our own citizens, not foreign traitors."

With that, Lieutenant Avot let himself out of Nordling's office and left the man to make plans for the fame and fortune he dreamed awaited him.

Saint-Cloud, France. October 1944.

Heddy was always wary of her father when he was working. Although he could, at times, be quite aloof with his daughter when *not* in work mode, he would more often than not make a little time for her. But, when he was busy with his business affairs and had on his *work face*—as Mother called it—Heddy found him to be distracted at best, cold and dismissive at his worst.

She knew Father was not only upset about leaving their beautiful apartment, but also by the fact he was unable to help the many charitable causes he had patronized over the years. Heddy had always been so proud that her father would send money to almost all of the orphanages and poor people who wrote on an almost daily basis to him asking for help; he had the power to change lives with the flourish of a pen upon his checkbook, and Heddy thought he never seemed happier than when he was doing so.

Oscar Frosell's influence as a warm and most generous man when it came to helping others went a long way toward ensuring his daughter did not grow up to be spoiled. In fact, for all the family's vast wealth, Heddy had been taught to appreciate the small things in life and to give thanks for the fact that she was far better off than so many others. Indeed, during their time in Paris, the sweet, generous little girl would often give away some of her toys and dolls to visiting children she understood to be less better off than herself. And, although it gave her a good feeling to see how much joy her actions brought, that was not what motivated her to do it. Quite simply, Heddy had been indoctrinated into a life of generosity by her father, for whom it was just a way he could give back and spread a little of his vast wealth to the less fortunate.

Even at such a tender young age, Heddy admired the way her father spread his considerable wealth around to the needy. In her eyes, it made him all the more awe-inspiring and intimidating. Having said that, Heddy had no way of understanding that not all recipients of her father's generosity were quite as deserving as others. As with any great philanthropist, Oscar Frosell attracted more than his fair share of vultures and hangers-on once word got around among the more unscrupulous members of Paris's society about how generous he could be with his money and possessions. It was also an unfortunate consequence of Frosell's charitable nature that it fostered envy among some; it was largely because of those crooked few that his family found themselves in their inopportune predicament. And still, through it all, when Oscar Frosell was made aware of the dire situation, Heddy would overhear her dear father lament to her mother about how many poor, unfortunate people were suffering because the loss of the family fortune at the hands of the wicked, greedy French meant he was unable to offer any means of help.

And, of course, the unfortunate thing about the whole sorry affair— as her father was wont to call it—was that it made him all the more inaccessible to Heddy. That had a profound impact on the little girl as she grew up around his obsession for justice; it made her deeply sad and had her feeling as if much of the time he wasn't there—even when he was.

He'd been on the telephone for most of the morning, and Heddy had been banished to the expansive gardens surrounding the villa with only her tricycle and imagination for company. She'd heard Father's raised voice on more than one occasion, and even though she'd been unable to make out his exact words, she could easily tell from the sharp tone to his voice there was something he was far from happy about.

The V2 was no longer in the villa's front garden, having been taken away shortly after Heddy and her family arrived at Saint-Cloud. All that remained of the bomb was a huge, ugly tear in the otherwise neat lawns and well-trimmed bordering shrubbery. The army had sent out their best bomb disposal experts to defuse the thing, and Heddy had been most disappointed she and her parents had been made to drive into the village and stay there until they got the all-clear the V2 had been disarmed and made safe—she'd wanted to watch the handsome young men at work as they heroically risked their lives to save hers.

They'd carted the V2 away on the back of a huge gray truck a day or two after that, and Heddy found she quite missed the old girl. To her young imagination, it was not a flying bomb from Germany, but a mysterious rocket from way across the darkest regions of space, perhaps even as far away as Mars. She'd often heard her father talk about the famous radio broadcast of *War of the Worlds*, which had created widespread panic across America in the year before she was born. Father would often begin his telling of the story with the preface that the Americans were one heck of a gullible race of people.

It began to drizzle, so Heddy made her way indoors. She would have much preferred to stay out to play in the groove created by her beloved alien space rocket, but knew from experience that all too soon it would turn into a muddy hole, and Mother would get upset with her for dirtying her pretty yellow dress.

". . . requisitioned by order of General Bouscat," she heard her father say as she made her way through to the kitchen. His voice was still raised, and she could clearly hear the bitter resentment edging his tone. "What on earth is the French Air Force doing requisitioning private property?"

"I'm sure it's all just some big misunderstanding." Marie attempted to soothe her husband's rising temper, although she knew it was most likely a battle lost before she'd even begun. "You'll soon get it all sorted out, I'm sure."

Frosell snorted and chewed on his cigarette holder as plumes of smoke from his dying cigarette swirled about his handsome face. "Our apartment—our *home*—was supposed to be under the protection of Sweden. It was all dealt with by the Swedish general consul himself." He plucked the cigarette stub from the holder and, in one fluid motion, inserted its successor, lit it, and sucked hard on the onyx. "Dzeroginsky says there's supposed to be a special authority set up in freed Paris to deal with such matters, but he's struggling to get any meaningful answers from *anyone*."

Frosell had commissioned the services of one Josef Dzeroginsky not long after he and his family had fled from the old folks' home to Saint-Cloud. Dzeroginsky was an experienced Polish lawyer with a fearsome reputation for being incredibly ruthless, especially when it came to dealing with government bureaucracy. He was also rumored to be quite fearless when faced with the higher echelons of authority—government officials included; he was precisely the right legal mind to be fighting in the Frosells' corner. Widely known around Paris, although seldom discussed, was that Dzeroginsky had lost much of his immediate family in the Nazi death camps, and he'd barely managed to escape Krakow by the skin of his teeth.

"Apparently he's unearthed some important information he thinks I should know," Frosell told his wife, "and he thinks it's time we began to seek restitution from the French for the loss of our property and belongings."

"Is that wise?" Marie couldn't hide her concern. "With everything they are saying about you?"

Frosell shook his head. "Everything we own is in Rue Dufrenoy," he told her. "Our art, our jewelry, our money . . . everything our families have worked so hard for. Unless we want to live out the rest of our lives like paupers and common criminals, there really is no other choice."

A look of fear crept across Marie Frosell's face. She screwed up the tea towel she held tight in her hands, twisting the thing into a taut knot. "Surely you can't possibly mean you intend to take on de Gaulle? He's proved himself to be quite invincible."

Frosell drew on his cigarette and inhaled its pungent smoke deep inside his body. "Marie, my darling," he said, "I have done nothing wrong. Everything being said about me is nothing more than malicious gossip and conjecture, and most of that based upon a job I never even took up." As he spoke, wispy clouds of white-gray smoke curled out of his mouth and drifted upward across his face like some ghostly mask. "And, if anyone can challenge the French and their renowned love of bureaucracy, it's Josef Dzeroginsky." There was a certain finality to his words that didn't solicit argument. "I have an appointment with him this afternoon; I think it's time I explored our options."

"You're going to Paris?" Marie was startled. "Are you sure that's wise, Oscar?"

Frosell gave his wife a reassuring smile. "I wouldn't be going if I thought otherwise." He crossed the room to hold her. "As long as I stay away from the apartment, I'll be fine." At that, a look of deep sadness settled on Frosell's handsome features. "Just listen to me," he groaned. "I sound so damn *guilty.*"

Law Offices of Josef Dzeroginsky, Rue de Cygne, Paris.

"*Dumesnil?*" Frosell barked. "Are you sure?"

Dzeroginsky huffed and sat himself down behind his wide, meticulously tidy mahogany desk. "I'm afraid that's what my research has dug up. I'm so sorry, Monsieur Frosell."

Frosell sat down heavily in the high-backed leather chair opposite his lawyer. Reaching into his pocket for a cigarette, he was very much in need of the warm comfort of its smoke.

Josef Dzeroginsky was a tall, wiry man in his middle age, although his prematurely grayed hair gave him the appearance of someone a decade or so older. He wore a neatly trimmed salt and pepper beard that accentuated the deep creases that wrinkled around his mouth when he pursed his thin lips. The man looked every inch the archetypal Polish lawyer in his expensive dark gray suit, and while he exuded a cold, calculating professionalism, his hazel eyes carried a sad, haunted look.

"The admiral and his good lady wife visited with Police Commissioner Richeaux," Dzeroginsky read from a pile of hastily scribbled notes on his desk. "At the Porte Dauphine Commissariat . . . on the sixteenth of last month."

"That was just before—" Frosell's words stuck in his throat.

"Alla Dumesnil took it upon herself to commandeer your apartment," Dzeroginsky filled in. "They accused you of being both a German *and* a Gestapo agent," he added. "Now you see why I wanted to speak to you about this in person."

"And precisely why I intend to seek restitution from the French government," Frosell said. "They have entirely ignored due process *and* the protection of the Swedish consulate."

Here, Dzeroginsky sniffed—loudly. "There is a possibility the consulate has some part in this." He tested the water with Frosell. "Perhaps it's just insomuch as they turned a blind eye to what the

French are doing, or perhaps it's something more. Either way, I have intelligence the general consul himself may well be complicit."

"Nordling," Frosell spat.

Dzeroginsky nodded. "The one and the same," he said. "It seems he and the admiral are quite good friends."

Frosell looked across the expensive desk at the thin-faced lawyer. The man had garnered the reputation of being the best property lawyer in all of Paris, if not the whole of France; his astronomically high fees certainly led one to believe it! And that was specifically why Frosell had sought him out—he knew tackling the new French government would be no easy task, and he needed the best legal mind on his side. "If Dumesnil's daughter is occupying my property illegally, surely it should be straightforward enough to remove her?"

The lawyer shook his head. "That's already been tried, Mr. Frosell," he said. "She was back in within the week—by order of General de Gaulle himself."

The mention of the general's name knocked the wind out of Frosell. Hands trembling, he nearly managed to maneuver his cigarette into the holder, light it, and take a hit of wonderfully calming smoke. "How on earth is de Gaulle involved in this?"

For once, Dzeroginsky was stumped. He shrugged his gaunt shoulders. "No idea on that one, but my educated guess would be Alla Dumesnil has the right connections."

Frosell sighed. Suddenly, the whole issue of restitution had become a lot more complicated. "Even so," he said, "the French have broken international law by allowing the requisition of property of a non-national from a neutral country—even if it was in wartime."

"You are right, of course." Dzeroginsky's sage voice sounded wise beyond his years. "Which is why I suggest we meet with the Second Bureau to clear matters up."

"The Secret Service?" Frosell was somewhat taken aback. "Why on earth should I meet with them? Are they involved in this?"

"I understand a Lieutenant Avot has been investigating," the lawyer replied.

"Investigating what, exactly?"

"I'm afraid to say, it's you, Mr. Frosell," Josef Dzeroginsky explained quietly.

CHAPTER NINE

Offices of the Second Bureau, Paris. October 20ᵗʰ, 1944.

At a little before three p.m., the light sprinkle of rain was beginning to ease up, and a faint rainbow smiled above Paris. Lowering his umbrella, Oscar Frosell made his way into the foreboding offices of the Second Bureau—the intelligence arm of the French Secret Service. Dzeroginsky had offered to accompany him, but Frosell had assured the lawyer it would be entirely unnecessary.

"I'd much rather spend my money on having you figure a way out of this mess than holding my hand," he'd said at the time. Frosell was more than confident in his belief that the innocent had nothing to fear.

"A wise decision, Monsieur Frosell," Dzeroginsky had replied with a wry smile playing about the corners of his narrow mouth. "It's obvious all they want is some more information from you about your supposed business with the Germans—all straightforward stuff, really—and Lieutenant Avot has given his personal word of honor no harm will come to you, since you are voluntarily attending his offices for questioning."

The phrase "word of honor" resonated badly with Frosell. In his experience, men who used it to reassure more often than not tended to be hiding something.

"Just remember, he and General Consul Nordling may well be very good friends," Dzeroginsky had reminded him. "So please be careful what you say."

"I only met Nordling the once," Frosell had told him. "I have no idea who his friends are."

So there he was, alone and, despite his earlier confidence, feeling much as if he were Daniel about to walk into the lion's den.

"Come in, come in!" Lieutenant Avot greeted Frosell with warmth, almost as if he were an old school friend and they had much to catch up on. "Thank you for coming," he said as he ushered Frosell into a spacious, wood-paneled office a short walk from the main concourse.

"You're more than welcome." Frosell took a seat.

Avot closed the door behind them and made himself comfortable behind his impressive desk. "Can I get you a drink?" he asked.

Frosell shook his head. "Do you mind . . . ?" He pulled out his cigarette case and offered it across the desk to Avot.

"*Merci*." Lieutenant Avot helped himself to one of Frosell's cigarettes. "You are well traveled, yes?"

"I have traveled extensively on business, yes," Frosell replied.

Avot said nothing. He lit up the cigarette with an American-brand lighter and then opened up a pristine beige file that lay neatly in front of him. Slowly, he began to flick through the neatly printed notes that populated it. "Africa, the Far East, India, Turkey . . ." He paused to suck on his cigarette.

Frosell frowned at the agent. "As I said, my business has taken me all over—"

"*Germany.*" Avot stopped there. He exhaled a lungful of smoke with a long, rattling wheeze and eyed Frosell from across the desk as one would an odd, unfamiliar specimen under the scrutiny of a microscope.

"That was a long time before the war—'35, I believe."

Avot's telephone rang. Its harsh, jangling bell startled both him and Frosell. Lifting up a hand by means of apology to Frosell, the lieutenant snatched up the receiver. "Avot," he growled.

Frosell sat quietly as Avot had a brief, decidedly one-sided conversation; all he did was listen intently to whoever was on the other end of the line. Then, after no more than a minute or so, he placed the receiver back on its cradle and the phone rang off with a quiet *ting.*

"Major Thomas would like to see you," Avot told Frosell in a most matter-of-fact manner.

"And he would be . . . ?"

"FFI." Avot frowned.

Frosell was puzzled by this turn of events. He'd attended the Second Bureau's offices at his own volition, ostensibly to clear up the confusion about his supposed work with the Germans, and now the chief of the *Forces Francaises de l'Interieur* wanted to see him? Exactly where de Gaulle's erstwhile resistance fighters came into the equation was a little beyond him at that juncture, although this was by no means the first time he'd heard the general's name mentioned in relation to Rue Dufrenoy. One thing was for sure, though, Frosell was beginning to think maybe he ought to have taken Dzeroginsky up on his offer to come along with him to the Bureau.

Avot stood up from his seat with a loud grunt. He grabbed his brown jacket from its back and ushered Frosell from the office. "My chief is waiting to see you," he said. "Please come this way." He then led Frosell down the brightly lit hallways to the office of Major Pierre Thomas.

Rapping on the major's door, Avot paused for his invitation to enter. Upon hearing the muffled voice from within, he opened the door and escorted Frosell inside.

"Oscar Frosell?" Major Thomas said, his sentence more of a statement than a question. "Your passport." He held out one hand.

"Pardon me?" Frosell was taken aback.

"Your *passport*," Thomas repeated, his arm outstretched and unmoving.

Frosell fished around in his jacket pocket for the passport he always carried there; in freed Paris, it was a necessity to be able to prove your identity at a moment's notice—it could sometimes make the difference between making it home or never being seen again. "Is there a problem here, Major Thomas?" he asked as he placed his passport into the man's slender hand.

Major Thomas ignored Frosell's question and opened up the passport. He screwed up his eyes as he leafed through each one of its pages in turn and seemed to closely scrutinize the multitude of customs stamps Frosell had earned on his many trips overseas.

"Is there something—?"

"This is false," the major barked. He held open the passport at the personal information page and shoved it toward Frosell's face—as if he were showing Frosell something he'd never seen before. "You are not Swedish as it states here, Monsieur Frosell," he growled. "You are, in fact, German *and* an agent of the Gestapo."

"I can assure you that neither of those is the case," Frosell replied. He glanced across at Avot, who raised an eyebrow but chose to remain silent. "If you would care to verify my nationality with the Swedish consulate . . ."

Thomas made an odd grunting sound, a snort of derision. He plucked a sheet of paper from his desk and held it aloft. "General Consul Mr. Nordling does not recognize you as Swedish, monsieur," Thomas declared. "Therefore you have a falsified passport. As such, you are arrested for impersonating a Swede."

The two FFI agents had clearly been waiting outside the major's office. With no discernible cue, yet with impeccable timing, they burst through the door and seized Frosell by an arm each.

"No!" Frosell protested, his voice vehement. "You have no jurisdiction to charge me with anything! *You can't do this!*" He turned to Avot for assistance, but Avot cast his eyes toward his superior officer.

"We *can* do this, Monsieur Frosell," Thomas told Frosell with more than a little relish. "And we will. And we will not rest until every German *collaborateur* has been rounded up and punished according to their crimes against France." He gave Frosell a wry smile. "Your money and fake passport are not going to save you. There'll be no buying your way out of this one, monsieur," he said. Then, to his agents, "Take him away."

And so, with no due process whatsoever, Oscar Frosell was unceremoniously bustled away and thrown into jail for the first time in his life.

CHAPTER TEN

D.G.E.R. prison, Boulevard Suchet, Paris. October 27th, 1944.

For a lawyer, Dzeroginsky looked remarkably out of place in the prison meeting room. His tall, gaunt frame appeared most awkward, and he adopted a hint of a stoop as he walked, as if to make himself a little more invisible in the grim surroundings. "You're looking well, Mr. Frosell," he greeted his client with an untruth.

Frosell snorted and gave the man a half smile. "I'm sure I've looked better." He knew his face looked pinched and somewhat sallow, and the unflattering gray prison uniform hung slack from his frame. It had only been a week since his arrest, but that's what a barely edible diet and one hour of sunlight a day will do to a man.

His resolve, however, was as unerring as always.

"How are Marie and Heddy holding up?" Frosell asked. "I've heard nothing since they took me from Major Thomas's office." He had been forbidden—on the orders of Major Thomas himself—to receive visits from his wife and lawyer; Dzeroginsky was only allowed to visit that day because he'd pulled a hell of a lot of strings and called in a favor or two.

Dzeroginsky gave what he clearly hoped was a reassuring smile. "They are as well as can be expected." He fidgeted in his seat. "Given the circumstances, of course."

"Of course." Frosell's heart sank at the thought of his wife and daughter all by themselves, although he did have the consolation that the D.G.E.R. had left them well alone. He knew, too, they were far safer alone in Saint-Cloud than they would have been at the apartment, or the godforsaken old folks' home Nordling had sent them to.

Nordling—the mere thought of the treacherous man's name had Frosell's hackles rising.

"I understand the D.G.E.R. cross-examined you." Dzeroginsky got straight down to business. He pulled out a pack of cigarettes—it was open and half empty, as the guard at the prison's imposing front gate had helped himself to a handful as the lawyer checked in.

Delighted, Frosell took the crumpled packet from Dzeroginsky and plucked out a cigarette. He'd had to make one pack last the entire time he'd been in jail, and some of those he'd had to trade with his cellmate for soap. "They asked me questions about my nationality," he said, "if that's what you mean." He carefully placed the cigarette between his lips and leaned over the table for Dzeroginsky to light it.

"Did you admit your father was Swedish?" the lawyer asked. He was still angry he'd not been informed about the interrogation. By law, he was supposed to have been in attendance. But, then again, *by law*, Oscar Frosell had no business being incarcerated in the first place.

"Of course." Frosell sucked on the cigarette as if it were his last; without the cool caress of the onyx holder, its tip felt unnaturally warm against his lips. "What would have been the benefit of denying the truth?"

Dzeroginsky nodded. "You are right, of course." He was a firm believer in the truth always being the best course of action. If only the French had shared that simple philosophy, he wouldn't be sitting opposite an innocent in a dismal little room with a table and two chairs bolted to its floor. "They've had a team of four agents digging deep into your background," Dzeroginsky said. "And still they've found nothing." He held his hands up in the air to emphasize his frustration. "They'll be back to talk to you soon enough, no doubt."

Frosell sighed and stretched his legs out beneath the table. "Armand, the man I share a cell with," he said, "now, he is a *true* collaborator. He fed intelligence to the Nazis just to stay alive, and now he spends his nights dreaming of Madame Guillotine. I actually feel quite sorry for him."

"That's nothing you need worry about, Mr. Frosell," Dzeroginsky reassured. "There is no way these trumped-up charges will ever stick. We will have you out of here in no time at all."

"It's already been seven days without charge, Josef." Frosell gave the lawyer a sardonic smile. "I'd hardly call that *no time at all.*"

Dzeroginsky smiled back. While he carried an absolute belief in the new French justice system, a small part of him feared for his client; there were people high up in the food chain whose best interests would be served well should Oscar Frosell meet with an untimely end. "Trust me," he said, "the Second Bureau have their best people on the case, and for as hard as they are trying, they have not found a single thing they could even begin to twist into something nefarious."

"Even the corrupt need plausible deniability, it would seem." Frosell laughed—it was such a strange noise to hear in such a place, and was quickly muted within the cold, gray confines of the prison room.

A bang on the metal door made both men jump.

"Time is up, *collaborateur*!" the gruff voice of the prison guard snaked through the tiny grille in the door.

Dzeroginsky huffed and shot a glance toward the door as the burly young man swung it open; the metal hinges let out a loud, grating squeal.

"Don't worry, I've become accustomed to it," Frosell said with a shrug of his shoulders. "Guilty until proven innocent—that appears to be the new system of justice in Paris these days." He stood up. "Thank you for coming, Josef," he said. "And thank you for these." He handed back the cigarette packet, having removed all but two.

The lawyer held up a hand. "They are for you," he protested. "I can easily buy more."

"Please," Frosell insisted, "take it." His eyes met Dzeroginsky's for only a heartbeat, and a look passed between the two men.

"Very well," Dzeroginsky conceded. He then turned to the guard, who stood at his shoulder, fingers drumming with impatience on the baton hanging from his belt. "You try to do something nice for a client . . . what can I say?" He stuffed the packet into the inside pocket of his jacket and got to his feet.

The guard said nothing. Instead, he nodded his head toward the door and held out a hand to usher the lawyer from the room.

"Goodbye, Monsieur Frosell," Dzeroginsky bid a sad farewell to his client. "Rest assured I am doing all I can to have you released without charge; I have high hopes the next time we meet, it will be over chicory and croissants at the *Café de la Paix*."

"I shall look forward to that, Monsieur Dzeroginsky." Frosell watched as his lawyer sauntered from the room. He couldn't shake the gnawing feeling in the pit of his stomach it would be quite some time before he would be outside in Paris and drinking chicory as a free man.

Dzeroginsky waited until he was outside and well out of sight of the prison gates before he fished the cigarette packet from his pocket. He pulled out the pair of cigarettes Frosell had returned to him and fished around inside the flimsy box with trembling fingers.

At the bottom of the cigarette packet, his fingers happened upon a small, neatly folded slip of paper. Upon further investigation, Dzeroginsky saw it was a cigarette paper. It had been carefully divested of its tobacco and meticulously folded into as small a square as possible. More than a tad paranoid, the lawyer glanced around, half expecting to see the looming figure of a prison official—or, even worse, a D.G.E.R. agent—making their way purposefully toward him.

Thankfully, the street was all but deserted, with Dzeroginsky's car being the only one parked within sight of the prison; one of the perks of being a lawyer was he didn't have to adhere to the prison's strict visiting times imposed upon a prisoner's families and friends.

Nonetheless, Dzeroginsky climbed into his car and locked the doors before carefully unfolding the cigarette paper.

The handwriting, although small, spidery, and marred by smudges, was unmistakably Frosell's. Dzeroginsky smiled and nodded as he read the concise instructions his client had written down in neat, impossibly straight lines.

> *Marie, you must pay a visit to the Swedish Legation in Paris*
> *(I learned it has now been reestablished). Inform them of my*
> *position and tell them they must arrange a meeting here with*
> *the Military Police Authorities as soon as is possible. Oscar.*

"You are a clever man, indeed, Monsieur Frosell," he muttered beneath his breath. With yet another paranoid glance over his shoulder, Dzeroginsky tucked Frosell's note back into the cigarette packet, which he returned to the safety of his inside pocket. He then started up his car, crunched it into gear, and set off in the direction of Saint-Cloud.

CHAPTER ELEVEN

D.G.E.R. prison, Boulevard Suchet, Paris. November 4th, 1944.

Against Frosell's expectations, Marie managed to convince the Legation to arrange the meeting as he'd requested. His headstrong wife could be incredibly persuasive when she put her mind to it.

And so, once again, Oscar Frosell found himself in the tiny room with the metal door and the furniture secured to the floor. As dismal and claustrophobic as the meeting room was, Frosell found it a welcome relief from staring at the brick walls of his cell and listening to Armand's constant weeping and protestations of innocence; even in the relatively short amount of time Frosell had shared the cell with the poor man, Armand's mental and physical health had deteriorated to such an extent he very much doubted the man would survive long enough to stand trial—assuming the new French government afforded him that luxury, of course.

Crammed into the hopelessly inadequate room along with Frosell was Dzeroginsky; Mr. de Belfrage, the Swedish chargé d'affaires; the four D.G.E.R. officers who had been assigned the task of unearthing Frosell's supposed murky past, his business dealings, and any proof of him being a Gestapo agent; and his beloved Marie. Of course, she had not brought Heddy along; the girl was back at the villa with the tutor Marie had employed to ensure the girl's education didn't suffer because of all the upheaval. It had been two long weeks since Frosell had laid eyes on his wife, and simply having her there in the room filled his heart with hope. He also knew his wife well enough to know she was not one who would simply sit at home hoping her husband would be released; she would be out fighting against the injustice and hassling absolutely everyone responsible for his arrest.

"Monsieur Frosell," one of the Second Bureau agents began, "I have scoured the whole of France and investigated all of your business dealings since 1937, but I have found nothing that could possibly be held against you." He eyed the others in the room; clearly he was uncomfortable beneath such scrutiny. "But there is absolutely nothing we can do as long as your own consul general continues to deny your Swedish nationality." His eyes flicked toward de Belfrage, who sat stony-faced and said nothing.

Frosell spoke up. "What is behind this travesty?" he demanded. "Why do I feel as if I am being conspired against?"

"You're rich, Mr. Frosell," the agent gave the simple reply. "We have taken the liberty of valuing your home and its contents, and it's actually worth quite a bit." His understatement hung in the room like a bad smell.

Suddenly interested in the agent's candor, Frosell cast a glance in Dzeroginsky's direction. The lawyer gave him a barely perceptible nod and scribbled a few choice words down on the notepad in front of him.

"And exactly how much did you make my confiscated property out to be worth?" Frosell pressed the agent, who was by now looking to be well out of his comfort zone. He figured the man would have been much less inclined to speak had he not been in the presence of Dzeroginsky and de Belfrage.

"With everything taken into consideration," the agent told him, "the furniture, carpets, pictures, and other art treasures, we valued at around two hundred million francs." He paused there, as if the enormity of the number had stolen his voice. "Money, jewelry, gold and platinum bars, etcetera . . . one hundred million francs. Your stamp collection was valued at around the same. All in all, Monsieur Frosell, we estimate your net worth to be somewhere in the region of four hundred million francs."

The agent's words settled across the eight people in the room, all of whom sat in silence awhile, the only sound being that of Dzeroginsky's pen as it skittered furiously across his notepad.

"And would you be able to give me that official valuation in writing, please?" Frosell pushed. His mind was already racing ahead to future claims for compensation against the French state.

The agent snorted and gave Frosell a half laugh. "Never in your life, monsieur," he replied. "But I have now confirmed it orally in front of a Swedish authority." He nodded toward de Belfrage. "And that is as much as I am prepared to do. I would also like to state that, had General Consul Raoul Nordling not denied your Swedish nationality in the first place, none of us would be sitting here today."

"Well," de Belfrage spoke up, "I can officially attest, without a shadow of a doubt, that Oscar Frosell is, indeed, a Swedish citizen." He tapped a finger on the envelope, which sat facing upward on the table before him and was adorned with the seal of the Swedish Embassy.

"Thank you, Monsieur de Belfrage." Dzeroginsky lifted his head up from his copious note taking. "I'm sure that has cleared matters up to everyone's satisfaction"—he nodded sagely and smiled at Marie—"and hopefully put an end to the wholly unfounded and malicious accusations toward my client."

Frosell let out a huge sigh of relief. With his nationality no longer under question—and scrutiny—he could finally return home to his family and make preparations with Dzeroginsky for the compensation he knew he was, without a doubt, due from the French.

The French, however, had other plans for Oscar Frosell.

CHAPTER TWELVE

Fort de Charenton Internment Camp. December 20th, 1944.

If such a thing were possible, the internment camp was slightly *more* welcoming than the Boulevard Suchet jail. Although he was now sharing a cell with three men instead of poor Armand, Frosell was afforded more time to himself, along with extra recreational time out in the high-walled exercise yard—that much was something, at least.

Built in 1842 for the then astronomical sum of five million francs, and first used as a prison six years after that, Fort de Charenton had most recently been occupied by the Germans. They'd used it as a radio transmitting station and ammunition dump all the way up until August 1944—the 25th, to be precise—when they'd quickly abandoned it as the Allies advanced on Paris. Oscar Frosell had the dubious honor of being among the first occupants as Charenton resumed service as a prison for political prisoners and juvenile delinquents, an eclectic mix he thought to be most peculiar. Of the former group, Frosell had come upon some who were guilty as all hell in their treachery against France, others whose supposed crimes he thought to be doubtful, and a disproportionate number of others—himself included—who were obviously innocent but who had fallen afoul of de Gaulle and his new regime.

There were signs of the Germans everywhere Frosell cared to look: German-labeled canned goods in the food store, scattered propaganda flyers and newspapers from the Motherland, and hastily scribbled words of defiance across the walls. The Germans, upon vacating their wartime home, had laid hundreds of tons of explosives around the fort. They were all hooked up to acid-fused detonators, which were timed to welcome the approaching Allied forces. And even that last show of German insolence had been thwarted, however, as the world-renowned bomb disposal expert, Roger Francois, had easily defused the bombs. Frosell reckoned the French would most likely put up a plaque in the man's honor one day.

Frosell had been given no explanation as to why he'd been moved to Charenton. Following the meeting with de Belfrage and the Second Bureau agents, everything had been all smiles and friendly handshakes. Frosell had thanked Dzeroginsky and kissed Marie a fond *au revoir*. The understanding in the room had been, following de Belfrage's attesting to his nationality, that as soon as the necessary paperwork was completed, Oscar Frosell would be a free man.

But that same day, somewhere around midnight, the D.G.E.R. had somewhat brusquely dragged Frosell from his cell, bundled him into one of their official anonymous vehicles, and transported him out of Paris to the internment camp.

Frosell sighed. He craved a cigarette—the one-pack-per-week allotment he'd received at Boulevard Suchet had been halved, and he'd needed to trade even most of those for a few basic provisions—but he managed to keep his mind occupied most of the time by working on miniature carvings of boats for his daughter.

He used old matches he'd saved up from the sparse few cigarettes he did manage to treat himself to, and those he found scattered around the exercise yard by his fellow prisoners—they clearly had no idea as to the value of those tiny strips of wood. Frosell had purloined a spoon from the mess hall—knives and forks were strictly forbidden, so he and the other prisoners, young and old, were forced to eat their meals like toddlers—and sharpened one side of it up on the cold stone floor of his cell. Occasionally, Frosell would find a sliver of wood chipped from the prison's stairs—Adolphe Thiers, the fort's designer, had deemed them a lavish, but necessary touch—which would make an excellent hull for a warship or single mast fishing boat. Each model was no longer than one and a half to two inches long, yet Frosell carved them precisely to scale and with the most intricate detail; for him, nothing short of absolute perfection would do.

Heddy would absolutely love them; he knew that much for certain, for she shared his passion for perfection—which is why, even from a tender young age, he had always demanded the best from the girl.

Of course, Frosell missed his family terribly. The long, cold days at Charenton gave him far too much time to dwell upon being apart from Marie and Heddy, even with the welcome distraction of the models and occasional lively political debate with his cellmates. His wife was an incredibly strong woman, especially in the face of adversity, and Frosell knew she would be coping fine without him. She would be missing him too, but she was always one for putting on a brave face in front of their daughter. Marie was a fearsome woman when she put her mind to it, and Frosell had heard, far from sitting idle, she had been hounding the Swedish consulate and making a nuisance of herself in every relevant French department. Her reputation had become enough to instill fear at the mere mention of her name!

Heddy had her tutor, who was a bright young thing from Saint-Cloud, and her education was coming along with aplomb—what with that and her rampant imagination, Frosell sometimes wondered if she would have noticed her father was gone at all!

Often, Frosell would think about his time in the D.G.E.R. jail and the meeting with Major Thomas that had landed him there. Clearly the whole thing had been a complete setup with strings being pulled from high up, but he'd never for a minute imagined he'd end up in an internment camp alongside genuine traitors and collaborators. And in the darkness of his many sleepless nights, Frosell would play over and over in his mind the brief conversation he'd had with *le greffier*—the registrar—upon first arriving at Boulevard Suchet; it was a conversation he'd dismissed at the time as little more than idle chitchat.

"I am sorry to see you here, Monsieur Frosell," the old man had said with a wry smile playing upon his pursed lips. A tired-looking man with thinning white hair and *pince-nez* spectacles, he'd been meticulously noting each one of Frosell's personal belongings the agents had relieved him of, along with Frosell's personal details— although with the information contained in Major Thomas's dossier,

Frosell wasn't sure what more *le greffier* could possibly have needed from him.

Frosell had fought to remain civil, but, since it was in his very nature, he'd replied, "And I am sorry to be here, monsieur. I'm hoping it will not be for too long."

"That, Monsieur Frosell, is entirely in your own hands."

"What do you mean by that?" Frosell's interest was stirred up. Was the man asking for a bribe to set him free?

"I hear you have been robbed, in effect, of four hundred million francs, monsieur." The old man hadn't once looked up from his paperwork, almost as if he were afraid to look Oscar Frosell directly in the eye.

"My property and belongings have been requisitioned, yes," Frosell told the registrar, "but it has all been one big misunderstanding."

"Much the same as you being here, no doubt?"

Frosell had nodded, even though the old man wasn't looking at him to see it. "Much the same as that, yes," he said.

"Give them fifty-fifty, Monsieur Frosell, and they will leave you alone," *le greffier* grunted. For the first time, he looked up from the neat handwriting in his ledger.

Nothing more was said between the two men. Frosell had wanted to press the old man to elaborate—did fifty-fifty mean what he understood it to mean? And *who* would leave him alone, and what more did they have in store for him? However, he was interrupted by one of the Second Bureau agents, who obviously had better things to be doing with his time than processing a prisoner.

The registrar's words hung heavy in Frosell's mind and had him fuming with the injustice of it all. He'd been falsely accused of the worst kind of treachery; driven from his home by the conniving admiral and his duplicitous friend, Raoul Nordling; had all his possessions illegally commandeered—no, *stolen*—by the very agents who were supposed to have been ensuring their safety; and incarcerated based upon nothing more than falsehoods and downright lies.

And all so that one Major Alla Dumesnil could be rewarded, according to the official paperwork Dzeroginsky had managed to dig up, for her "services to Air Marshall Bouscat."

Of course, being such a cynical soul, Frosell couldn't help but wonder exactly what *services* Admiral Dumesnil's daughter had administered to Bouscat that would warrant such a generous gift.

Frosell felt he had every right to be angry—he had lost everything, after all. He'd learned from his lawyer—two days after his wholly unexpected move from the D.G.E.R. jail—that since the meeting with de Belfrage, all of his private papers, letters, and documents had disappeared from Rue Dufrenoy, along with nearly all of his possessions. That had been the one and only time Frosell had spoken to anyone since entering Charenton. He had been kept completely isolated from the outside world since then.

Thoughts of restitution had begun to fill Frosell's every waking moment, even as he attempted to occupy his mind with the intricately carved boats. As obsessive as it was becoming, the boat making got him through the protracted, dismal prison days and in so many ways helped keep his sharp mind active and from going completely insane.

To hell with giving away half of the fortune he and his family had worked so hard to build up, he thought, especially to people who had done nothing to earn it except lie, cheat, and betray him.

Oscar Frosell's mind was quite steadfast. He was going to pursue the French government for full and complete compensation for everything they had taken from him, plus expose everyone involved for the scheming, disingenuous people they truly were—and if that list included his own general consul *and* General de Gaulle, then so be it!

Fort de Charenton Internment Camp. December 23rd, 1944.

"Oh, *merde*," the prison guard swore as he watched Marie Frosell storm across to his desk with Heddy close behind her; it was the woman's third time at the camp in as many days. "It is you again, madame."

Marie heard the man's complaint but chose not to acknowledge it; the one thing it told her was that her nagging was making some impact at the internment camp—hopefully it would be enough to garner her husband's release.

Heddy followed her mother without complaint. She had grown accustomed to the unpleasant places they were forced to frequent as Mother fought to have Father sent back home. In the space of only a few days, the poor girl had already been dragged around on trains and buses to the Swedish consulate and so many French government buildings she'd lost count. Then there were the police stations, and now the prison, all of which smelled damp and were as decidedly unpleasant as the people who worked in them.

Marie had quickly established herself as a nuisance—hence the guard at the front desk's rude exclamation within earshot of a small child. Heddy was especially proud that her mother could instill such fear into grown men—many of whom were far, far bigger than her—and she loved to watch how they all cringed when Mother raised her voice to demand to see someone in authority, or that she be taken immediately to visit her husband.

However, for as much as Heddy loved being supportive of her mother, she would have preferred to have been home playing with other children. The fact was not lost on Heddy that a little girl needed to be around friends her own age, and that was something sadly lacking in her life. Instead, she was being dragged from pillar to post with barely time to breathe between her mother's altercations with officials, politicians, lawyers, policemen, and prison guards. She was already feeling isolated following the family's sudden move from Paris, and her role as Mother's sole support had her retreating more and more into her shell.

"I must insist you release my husband straightaway," Marie demanded.

"You know I cannot do that, madame," the guard said. "I told you as much yesterday."

"I have signed papers from the consulate," Marie told him. "And from the police commissioner's office." As she rummaged about in her purse for the paperwork she'd hounded officials to sign, the guard struggled to his feet with a weary sigh.

"I can ask the warden to speak with you . . . again." He shuffled off in the direction of a narrow, arched doorway secreted behind his desk. "But he's going to tell you the same thing he told you yesterday—you will have to come back during regular visiting hours, and he doesn't have the authority to let Monsieur Frosell go just because you bullied him into it."

With a triumphant flourish, Marie produced the thin sheaf of papers from the bottom of her purse. "Well, we shall see about that, monsieur," she called after him.

Saint-Cloud, France. December 24th, 1944.

The Norwegian spruce was up in the corner of the living room and gaily decorated with homemade baubles. Heddy had helped, of course, and her haphazard array of decorations was dotted about the lower half of the tree—as high up as the little girl could reach. The rich, joyous sounds of Christmas carols wafted out from the wireless in the corner of the living room, to compete with the loud crackles and pops of the logs burning in the large stone fireplace.

For the first time in six years, Marie Frosell had decorated the Christmas tree without her husband. It had been a tradition of theirs since they married, and before Heddy came along. The mere thought of how much had happened since then was dizzying. The whole world had been upended and thrown into turmoil at the hands of the Germans and the Japanese, and her family was being torn apart by the greed of the French. Some days, all she wanted to do was lie down on the bed she should have shared each night with Oscar and cry, but Marie Frosell was made of much stronger stuff than that.

"Are you okay, Mother?" Heddy broke into her reverie.

Marie nodded at her daughter. "I'm just thinking about your father," she said. "Why don't you go ahead and open your gifts from Père Noël?" Oscar always insisted they observe the French tradition of opening Christmas gifts from Père Noël on Christmas Eve; he delivered them down the chimney when good little boys and girls weren't looking.

Heddy shook her head with such vigor, her entire body quivered. "I'm waiting for Father." Her voice was firm, and she was quite resolute on the matter. "He will be home soon, won't he, Mother?"

"I'm hoping so, Heddy," Marie said, although deep in her heart she feared otherwise. She peered out through the large picture window at the expanse of winter-deadened lawn and dormant bushes sprawling out from the rear of the villa; it seemed to her Heddy wasn't the only one who had put everything on hold to await Oscar's return.

Although the hour was not yet four, the weather had already grown quite gloomy. Dark gray clouds sat heavy and bloated in the winter sky, their bellies fat with the promise of snow. On any other occasion, both Marie and Heddy would be beyond excited at the prospect of snowmen and family snowball fights—Oscar Frosell happened to be a crack shot with a snowball—followed by steaming mugs of hot cocoa by the roaring fire. On any given year, that would all be typical Christmas faire for the Frosells. Only this year everything was so awfully different.

A knock on the front door startled Marie. Heddy jumped too. They had both grown to be jittery in the absence of the man of the house, especially given the circumstances of his absence.

"Perhaps Père Noël forgot to leave something for you?" Marie said to Heddy. She tried her best to hide the quiver in her voice, but her daughter had a tendency to be far too perceptive for her own good.

"Is it the policemen?" Heddy asked. "Or the admiral?" She'd picked up on her father's rants about Dumesnil, and the admiral and his wife had taken the place of the bogeyman in the Frosell household.

Marie said nothing and made her way to the door. "Stay here," she instructed Heddy with a tone that told the girl she *really* meant it.

Heddy stayed put.

Heart pounding, mouth dry, Marie Frosell put on her best smile and approached the door. With her husband's hasty and altogether unforeseen move to Charenton, Monsieur Dzeroginsky had warned her to expect a visit at any time from the police, or even the D.G.E.R.—he'd said they might use it as a tactic to put pressure on Frosell. That had struck Marie as an odd thing to say at the time, since they had blocked all attempts she'd made to see her husband—the lawyer's visits had been blocked too—and put pressure on him for *what*, exactly?

Luckily, to date, she and Heddy had been left alone.

Surely they wouldn't harass her on Christmas Eve, of all days? Then again, what better time to worry a mother left alone in a strange place with a young child?

Taking in a deep breath, the fixed smile hurting her face, Marie pulled open the heavy front door.

"Hello, Marie," Oscar Frosell greeted his wife. "Merry Christmas."

Marie all but fainted on the spot. In fact, she may well have fallen right there on the doorstep had her husband not caught her. He held her close in his strong arms, and even beneath the sour prison smell of damp desperation clinging to his suit, Marie took in the comforting scent of her beloved husband.

"Father!" Heddy raced along the hallway. She'd obeyed Mother's instruction right up until she'd recognized her father's sweet baritone voice. "I knew you'd come home for Christmas!" She ran into Frosell's one free arm and hugged him tight.

Frosell held his wife and daughter on the doorstep of the villa in Saint-Cloud. A deep, dark part of him had feared he'd never get to experience this moment, a part of him convinced he was destined to rot in the internment camp, or perhaps even to suffer a much worse fate. But, just as unexpectedly as the D.G.E.R. had bundled him off to Charenton in the middle of the night, the decision had been made to release him.

The decision had, apparently, been made due to "lack of cause," although Frosell would never find out who had made the decision.

They opened the gifts from Père Noël almost the minute Frosell had settled himself into the temporary home they'd made in the villa, and Heddy declared that Father was by far the best present he had brought that year—although the tiny boats he'd carved for her came in a close second. After what had seemed like a lifetime apart, Frosell savored every moment with his wife and daughter. It was true what they said: you never truly appreciate what you have until it's gone.

Frosell fished his cigarette holder from the prison-issue brown paper bag that contained the few belongings he'd had with him two months ago when he'd marched into Major Thomas's office with confidence and good intent. He inserted a cigarette from a fresh packet in his desk drawer and enjoyed the first decent smoke he'd had in a long time.

The Frosells enjoyed a wonderful Christmas. They relished one another's company, laughed and played together, and for the first time in a while, things seemed almost as back to normal as they could be.

And through it all, Oscar Frosell made ready his plans to challenge de Gaulle and the French nation for the unspeakable wrongs they had forced upon his family.

CHAPTER THIRTEEN

Café de la Paix, Paris. January 16th, 1945.

"My advice to you, as your lawyer, would be to take *le greffier*'s advice," Dzeroginsky said between slurps of rich chicory that more resembled mud from the Seine than a hot beverage. "He was quite obviously passing on a message from above."

Frosell leaned forward in his chair before speaking quietly; *walls have ears*, as Frosell's father had always been fond of saying. That insipid Nordling had said the phrase as well. Frosell shook off the bad memory of the Swedish general consul. He took a moment to collect his thoughts and calm his temper. Losing patience with one's lawyer could only ever be counterproductive.

"I thought I'd made myself perfectly clear, Josef." Frosell's tone was calm and measured. "I am *not* prepared to simply hand over fifty percent of my family's legacy to the French—or anyone else, for that matter. And besides which, it was never an official offer from the government—or anyone else for that matter."

Dzeroginsky sighed. It was not as if his client's stance was unexpected—as Frosell said, he *had* previously made it perfectly clear. However, there was always hope Oscar Frosell would see past his own stubbornness and see reason—no matter how vague that hope may be. "You are not so naïve as to believe the *greffier* was speaking on his own behalf, Oscar; what he said made good sense and most likely came from the very top. There's no doubt at all in my mind it would make all this . . . unpleasantness . . . go away, Monsieur Frosell."

It irked Frosell that Dzeroginsky still insisted on being so formal. He'd asked the man to call him Oscar numerous times at their first meeting and, despite agreeing, the lawyer had chosen to stick with *Monsieur Frosell.*

"But I have done nothing wrong," Frosell replied. "Why should I give in to what is essentially extortion to get myself acquitted from fabricated charges?" He blew on his chicory and took a hearty sip. The warmth of the liquid slid down into his stomach and spread through his body. "If anything, it is *they* who should be paying me!" His voice raised a little, and Dzeroginsky glanced around to see if they'd caught anyone's attention. Thankfully, on such a cold Paris afternoon, they were the only ones foolish enough to be outside.

"I understand your grievance," Dzeroginsky placated, "and at any other time, I would advise you to sue everybody involved—"

Frosell cut him off. "Until you've been accused of being Gestapo, a *collaborateur*, and having your nationality blatantly lied about by your own consul, I really don't think you can fully empathize, Monsieur Dzeroginsky," he spat.

The lawyer nodded. Let the man have his rant—it was the least he deserved, given what the French and Raoul Nordling had put him through. "These are extraordinary times," he continued once Frosell had calmed a little and the fire had dampened in his eyes. Dzeroginsky had seen such deep obsession before, usually in clients who were entirely in the wrong but believed themselves untouchable. In his experience, such obsession was often dangerous. "De Gaulle and his people are forging an entirely new France, which, given the debacle of the Vichy regime, is not an entirely bad thing, in my opinion." Inwardly, he flinched as he waited for Frosell's next tirade. It didn't come.

"People are being improperly imprisoned without due cause and process, just as you were, and a considerable number are not as lucky as you, Monsieur Frosell." The lawyer ran a hand through his thinning hair. "I know of several, personally, who were taken into the system and simply disappeared."

"So why wasn't I made to disappear?" Frosell asked. "Major Thomas certainly had the means to make it happen, along with whoever signed the order to have me shipped out to Charenton."

Dzeroginsky nodded along and hoped Frosell wouldn't ask the obvious question. To date, he'd still been unable to ascertain who'd given the order—to all intents and purposes, *no one* had. "Because you have something they want, monsieur," he replied. "And even in these tumultuous times, the disappearance or death of a national from a neutral country—especially such a wealthy individual as yourself—would not go unnoticed by the international community."

He slurped loudly at his chicory. "And General de Gaulle will not wish to have his new status as France's savior sullied by accusations of wrongdoing, especially when the Allies are itching to start hanging war criminals left, right, and center."

Frosell stiffened at the sound of de Gaulle's name. "That bastard is at the bottom of all this," he growled, "or the top, whichever way you care to look at it."

"Allegedly so," Dzeroginsky agreed, "but you'll never be able to prove that. The man is a national hero and, as such, he's pretty much untouchable."

"Then we attack those who are not." Frosell was at least pragmatic enough to realize the folly of launching a lawsuit for restitution against the man who had delivered France from the tyranny of Nazi Germany. "I want you to draw up the papers against Admiral Dumesnil for theft and defamation of character by spreading false rumors of a nature intended to cause harm." As always, Oscar Frosell had been meticulous in his research; such an accusation against a highly honored French admiral was grave indeed, and he knew it—hence the wording had to be precise. "And his daughter, Major Alla Dumesnil, for looting and the spreading of false rumors."

"Those are some serious allegations, Monsieur Frosell."

"Would you say they are unfounded?"

Dzeroginsky shook his head.

"And also, against Air Minister Charles Tillon, for misuse of authority."

The lawyer frowned at his client from across the table. He knew of Tillon, of course, but failed to see his place among Frosell's jigsaw puzzle of deceit. "Monsieur Tillon is very highly thought of. I don't see—"

"He was responsible for Air Marshall Bouscat's actions when he commandeered my home and belongings," Frosell told him. "And I want him held accountable."

Dzeroginsky eased back in his chair and groaned a little. For as much as he liked Frosell and empathized with the travesty of justice that had befallen him, this entire conversation was giving him a dull, gnawing sensation in his gut. Oscar Frosell was in the right, and there was absolutely no doubt about that at all. Lies *had* been told by people high up for their own nefarious means and outright greed, but Dzeroginsky was alarmed to be asked to sue government officials, well-respected admirals, and war heroes.

"I feel I must advise you, Monsieur Frosell—"

"*Damn* your advice, sir!" Frosell barked. "You are my lawyer, and these are my instructions—and if you're not prepared to act upon them, then I'm sure plenty of lawyers in Paris would love to take my money to do so."

Dzeroginsky flinched a little. In his experience thus far, Frosell had not been prone to such angry outbursts, although he was certainly more than entitled to. "Very well, Monsieur Frosell," he said, "I will start on the necessary paperwork straightaway; expect to have them ready to sign in twenty-four hours." He drained the last dregs from his chicory and made ready to leave. He thought his client foolish for not considering the idea of the fifty-fifty offer—be it official or otherwise. Two hundred million francs was still a considerable amount of money to keep, after all. He also though Frosell a tad too cavalier for making such big waves in the newly freed France. But then again, money talks.

True to his word, Josef Dzeroginsky had Frosell's papers ready to sign by the close of office hours the next day. He drove out to Saint-Cloud to have Frosell sign, and delivered them personally to the courts the day after.

And on January 18th, 1945, Oscar Frosell was arrested for the second time.

CHAPTER FOURTEEN

Saint-Cloud, France. January 18th, 1945.

Mesmerized, Heddy watched through the window as a half dozen police cars screeched up to the villa; in their rush, they tore up the gravel driveway and drove over the lovingly repaired lawn where the V2 rocket had created such a huge hole.

Mother was panicking, running around the villa with tears in her eyes, but Father remained his usual calm, stoic self; it would take more than a gang of *gendarmes* to ruffle Oscar Frosell's feathers! He peered through the curtains as the black vehicles rolled to a halt in front of the house and a small army of officers scrambled out and dashed toward the villa. As they ran, they jostled among themselves, as if in competition to be the first to knock on the Frosells' door. Heddy thought they looked like a bunch of silly penguins.

"Please, calm down, Marie." Frosell was doing his best to soothe his frantic wife's frazzled nerves; she was still reeling from his previous encounter with law enforcement, and the thought of her husband being taken away yet again terrified her. "It's intimidation, that's all; nothing to be worried about." He took Marie's hands and looked deep into her frightened eyes. "I guess my claim against the state for restitution has rattled the wrong cages—or the *right* ones, depending upon how you look at it." He offered what he hoped was a comforting smile.

They heard a hard, insistent thumping on the front door and harsh voices demanding that Oscar Frosell open up. Marie jumped and gripped her husband's hands. "I don't want to lose you, Oscar; I really don't think I could bear to go through all that again."

"If we're going to get through this, you must remain resolute." Frosell glanced across the room at Heddy, who appeared to be holding herself together rather better than her mother. At that moment, Frosell knew, no matter what happened to him, his wife would always have someone strong by her side. "The child needs to see her mother and father standing up for what's right—and, more importantly, against what's wrong—no matter how powerful the perpetrators are. *We* are the innocent victims here, Marie; don't ever forget that." Frosell let go of his wife's hands as Heddy scampered across the room to be close to her parents as the police grew ever impatient.

"*Open up!*"

"I'd better go before they kick the door down. Philippe would not be pleased if I allowed it to happen," Frosell said with a wry smile. He took a long, sucking draw at his cigarette to finish it off—he had no idea when the next time would be he'd be able to enjoy that particular pleasure—and ground its dying stub out in a nearby ashtray. "Stay here; neither of you need to see this." In a rare show of affection, he patted his daughter on the head and ruffled her hair a little. "Take care of your mother," he said.

"Yes, Father." Heddy grinned up at him, her eyes brimming with pride; this was still all very much make-believe for the young girl, and she felt grown up at the thought of taking care of Mother.

Striding from the room, Frosell gathered his hat and trench coat as he made his way to where the gendarmerie had finally quit thumping on the door and were no doubt deciding who was going to force it open. "Call Dzeroginsky," he instructed his wife. "His number is by the telephone. Tell him what has happened and they'll most likely take me back to Boulevard Suchet. And don't worry—he'll have me home in no time!"

Oscar Frosell smiled goodbye to his wife and daughter, opened up the front door, and, for the second time in his life, surrendered himself to the police.

D.G.E.R. prison, Boulevard Suchet, Paris. January 19ᵗʰ, 1945.

To say the whole thing was a farce would have been quite the understatement. After the police bundled Frosell into one of their cars, they sped him back to Paris. He'd been correct in his assumption they'd deposit him at the D.G.E.R. prison on Boulevard Suchet—and had him up before the makeshift kangaroo court before Josef Dzeroginsky even had the time to get himself there.

The self-same *greffier* greeted Frosell with a sly grin. Frosell regarded the old man with suspicion as he recalled the old man's earlier advice. And still, Oscar Frosell had absolutely no intention of allowing the French to bully him out of so much as one franc of his fortune, let alone fifty percent. "Bonjour, Monsieur Frosell." The registrar ran a gnarled hand through his shock of white hair. He slipped his narrow spectacles from his face and watched intently as Frosell went through the routine of emptying his pockets and depositing his few personal belongings onto the small metal table. "It is so very nice to see you again." A sardonic smile played across the old man's thin lips, and his dull eyes twinkled in the harsh light of the solitary bare bulb dangling above his head.

"Likewise, monsieur *le greffier*," Frosell replied. He hoped the man wasn't going to suggest the fifty-fifty deal again; he was welcome to keep the proposal to himself.

In what passed for a court, the prosecutor didn't look like a prosecutor at all. He was a young man no older than his late twenties—early thirties at best—who seemed to Frosell to be more than a little bewildered at the whole spectacle, as if he'd drawn the short straw and reluctantly found himself seconded to play the role at the last minute. The judge—one Adolphe Leblanc—was a bald, crusty old Frenchman who Frosell doubted was a real judge at all. Most likely he was ex-military, possibly air force, who had presided over court marshals and the shooting of traitors and deserters. He, too, had an air of weary bafflement about him, like he'd woken up to find himself not in his bed, but presiding over the hearing of an ex-Gestapo agent.

Had Frosell's liberty and personal fortune not been at stake, he'd have found the whole thing wonderfully comical—even something worthy of Chaplin himself!

"So, Monsieur Frosell," the young prosecutor read from a thin collection of papers he held in a trembling hand, "you were in Turkey—ostensibly on business—in 1941. Would you like to explain to the court the exact nature of that business?"

Frosell looked around. He eyed the judge and the quartet of D.G.E.R. agents who stood guard by the door; the courtroom was most unlike any one he'd ever been in before. "Am I being charged with something here?" he asked the prosecutor.

"Just answer the question, monsieur," Judge Leblanc growled. He made a show of looking at his watch, as if he had someplace more important to be.

Frosell sighed. After spending the night in a D.G.E.R. cell without charge or access to his lawyer, his patience was wearing thin. "Your information is a mistake, sir." He fought hard to remain civil; losing his temper with the young prosecutor wouldn't serve him well, even in such a joke of a courtroom. "I was in Paris for the whole of that year."

"Prove it." The prosecutor fiddled with the collar of his shirt; the young man seemed unaccustomed to formal wear, especially starched white shirts and paisley ties.

"According to common law, any accusation has to be proven by the prosecution," Frosell instructed. He was beginning to feel sorry for the young man; he was being paid—very little, no doubt—to read from notes that had obviously been badly researched and hastily put together, to say the least.

"You are quite right, Monsieur Frosell," the prosecutor replied after some deliberation. "But common law does not apply to traitors such as yourself."

"I am not a traitor. I am a Swedish citizen."

"That is immaterial." More words put into the prosecutor's mouth by whoever had typed out the notes. "You must prove your innocence. We *do not* have to prove you guilty." He glanced at what passed for the bench for reassurance. Judge Leblanc nodded sagely and looked at his watch again.

"I did not go to Turkey that year; you can take a look at my passport if you like."

"That's not saying much." The prosecutor was smug. "A traitor of your means could easily have entered the country illegally."

"So, ask the porter at Rue Dufrenoy. He can testify I wasn't away from home at all during 1941."

The young prosecutor fiddled with his collar and his youthful face reddened. "But you could bribe the porter to say anything you wished him to, Monsieur Frosell. It's all just a matter of price with people like you, isn't it?"

"The same argument holds true for your witnesses, monsieur." Frosell glowered at the young man and took no pleasure in seeing him cringe like a timid, cornered animal. "And may I ask who is trying so hard to prove I was in Turkey? And why?"

"That is a witness for the prosecution," the young man replied. "They are of sound character, and the prosecution's witnesses don't have to prove their integrity. You, on the other hand, Monsieur Frosell, do."

And so it went on. No witness for the prosecution was ever called, the young prosecutor's questions became ever more absurd, Judge Leblanc grew ever more bored with the whole charade, and Frosell's temper bubbled closer to the surface with each ill-conceived line of inquiry; this was what passed for justice in the newly liberated France, the country Frosell loved and had adopted as his own.

Eventually, after what seemed an impossible age, Dzeroginsky arrived—the D.G.E.R. clerks had deliberately held him up at the front desk with a whole string of petty, clearly contrived delays—and the makeshift court was adjourned.

Then they kept Frosell and his lawyer waiting over four hours in a stuffy, windowless room before *le greffier* was sent in to inform them the court had been dismissed and Frosell was free to go. There'd be no further questions, nor any charges, and by the way, perhaps Monsieur Frosell might wish to further consider signing over the fifty percent of his property and money to avoid any further unpleasantries?

Unable to contain his anger and afraid he'd say or do something he'd live to regret, Frosell simply walked out of the tiny room, away from the D.G.E.R. and Boulevard Suchet, and had Dzeroginsky drive him back home to his family.

CHAPTER FIFTEEN

Saint-Cloud, France. March 12th, 1945.

Marie Frosell fretted about her husband. Since returning from the D.G.E.R. jail two months earlier, he had become increasingly obsessed with gaining restitution from the French—even more than before. He'd told her little about what he'd been put through that day. Josef Dzeroginsky had kindly filled in a few of the details, although, of course, he had not been there through most of the charade—and the most Oscar had said was the whole courtroom drama had been based on little more than false accusations and outright lies. He did, however, interpret the affair as a sign of the Dumesnils, Nordling, Bouscat, and their cohorts—de Gaulle included—desperately trying to make things fit to justify their illegal actions. To Frosell, that could mean only one thing: he was on the right track to be reimbursed by the French for everything they had illegally confiscated.

And to that end, Frosell had informed Marie he fully intended to keep on pushing—as hard as he and Dzeroginsky possibly could.

News of the judgment in early February—the 5th to be exact—hadn't done much to dampen her husband's resolve. If anything, the fact that, in effect, it absolved the French from any responsibility—and, more importantly—liability, had made Oscar all the more determined to seek justice.

He'd summarized the pertinent parts for his wife. "The judgment states clearly the methods employed by Madame Dumesnil to get our apartment under her control were entirely in the wrong." He'd taken a long drag on his cigarette and cracked a wily smile. "Note how they've deliberately referred to her as *madame*, when we know she signed the requisition order as *Major* Dumesnil." Dzeroginsky had managed to obtain copies of the actual documents before the originals mysteriously disappeared; that fact had not been mentioned in the court documents. Of course it hadn't. "The court is saying she did so as a private person, which means neither the air minister nor the state can be held responsible."

At first, Marie was delighted. Surely a judgment laying blame firmly at the Dumesnils' door was a good thing? It meant the Frosell family could finally return to their family home on Rue Dufrenoy.

"If we go back there, we run the risk of being oppressed and bullied by the authorities again." It had pained Frosell to have to break the bad news to his poor wife. "The judgment safeguards the state from any claims for damages we may launch against it. *And* it acquits the Dumesnils of plundering and stealing."

Marie was devastated. "So *that's* why they put Alla's name as madame and not major?" The realization crept over her like a heavy, dark cloud. "There's nothing you can do, Oscar?"

He took another pull on yet another cigarette; the cherry at its end glowed bright orange. "I won't give up, Marie," Frosell said. "For your sake and Heddy's, I will never give up until we have back what is rightfully ours—and Charles de Gaulle be damned."

Then came another blow.

As if to rub the Frosell family's noses in the travesty of French justice they'd just been served, less than a few weeks after the judgment, *Le Monde*, *Journal du Commerce*, and most other Parisian newspapers carried the story of the marriage of Major Alla Dumesnil—daughter of the acclaimed admiral—to Captain Gillet Girardot, adjutant to Charles de Gaulle. The Paris wedding, held at Saint Eustache church, had been a most lavish affair and attended by politicians and dignitaries from all across France. The guest of honor had been General de Gaulle himself.

The news had driven Frosell to an even deeper level of obsession as he plotted and schemed at the villa with Dzeroginsky to find ways of circumnavigating the judgment. That de Gaulle was involved had the lawyer nervously questioning every objection his client raised, but Frosell simply wasn't going to take no for an answer. "There's got to be a way, Josef, there simply *has* to be. I refuse to accept this as the end of it. The French wanted at least half of everything. Now they have it all, and for what? Because General Consul Raoul Nordling was more concerned with looking after his own interests than those of the citizens it's his job to protect?"

Dzeroginsky had no option but to agree, even though he couldn't see how they wouldn't be beaten down at every turn. He argued with

Frosell—quite heatedly on occasion—but he was a good, decent man who hated to see such a miscarriage of justice served upon the Frosells through no fault of their own. Perhaps Oscar Frosell's biggest mistake had been in allowing the Dumesnils to force their unwanted friendship upon his family.

And so, under Oscar Frosell's instruction, Josef Dzeroginsky had once more drawn up the necessary paperwork to claim restitution for property seized, goods and chattels stolen, and served it to the Paris courts.

It was dark when the phone rang and woke Frosell. He and Marie had retired what seemed like hours before, although a quick glance at the bedside alarm clock told him it was only a little after midnight. Climbing quickly out of bed, he put on his dressing gown and slippers—there was a distinct chill in Saint-Cloud's mid-March air—and padded out to the lounge where the telephone's tinny trilling threatened to wake Marie and Heddy.

"Hello?" Frosell's stomach knotted. A phone call that time of the night was never going to be the harbinger of good news.

Silence.

Although he couldn't hear anything to demonstrate it, Frosell *knew* someone was on the other end of the line.

Finally, he heard, "Monsieur Frosell." It was not a question.

"Speaking. Who is this?"

"A friend." The voice was deep and carried a thick French accent Frosell suspected was fake. "The D.G.E.R. are on their way, Monsieur

Frosell. I suggest you make the necessary preparations for you and your family."

"Who is this?" Frosell asked again. He peered out through the thick velvet curtain and saw nothing but darkness.

"Get your family out of there now, monsieur." The line went dead.

Frosell dialed Dzeroginsky's number from memory; he figured he may as well get his lawyer from his bed, too.

Then Frosell roused Marie and Heddy from their deep sleep and, much to their protests, had them gather a few essentials into a small suitcase before ushering them quickly and quietly out to the car at the side of the villa. Heddy had to be carried; she was not one to be easily disturbed once asleep, and she'd curled up back in her bed the moment she'd thrown a few clothes and a favorite stuffed animal into the suitcase. Frosell maneuvered his daughter gently from her bed clothes and took her out to the car.

Lights appeared in the distance. They were obviously vehicle lights, and there was a veritable procession of them. Of course, given the late hour and the speed at which they were hurtling along the narrow country lane, the vehicles were obviously heading toward the villa.

"Hurry!" Frosell urged his wife as he placed Heddy gently along the back seat of the car. "We have to get going."

Marie screwed up her eyes against the dark in a vain attempt to make out what belonged to the harsh white lights that lit up the budding spring trees bordering the lane leading up to the villa. "Who is it, Oscar?"

"Either the police or the D.G.E.R. Either way, it would be best we were not home when they arrive."

"Not again?" Marie sounded most crestfallen, defeated.

She slid into the passenger seat as her husband gunned the engine and made ready for their escape. "Don't worry; it's nothing more than more intimidation. Dzeroginsky filed a new motion for restitution. This will be the state's reaction to it, nothing more."

"I didn't know you'd filed again."

"I didn't want you to worry, my love." Frosell patted his wife's knee to reassure her as he skillfully maneuvered the Dauphine toward the driveway that snaked away from the villa. "I called Dzeroginsky before I woke you—he was none too happy to be dragged from his bed at this ungodly hour, I can tell you—and he'll have papers drawn up to appeal against this harassment before dawn."

Frosell nudged the gas with his toe and pushed the car as fast as he dared in the dark. He had no idea where he would go at such a late hour of the night; all he wanted was to get his family away from the villa. As the car darted down the driveway, its headlights picked out all manner of twinkling eyes in the shrubs lining it and created dancing shadows, which stretched out into the darkness.

Suddenly, Frosell stomped on the brake. The car skidded to a juddering, grating halt that sent up a thick plume of dust and had Heddy tumbling from the back seat.

There, blocking the exit to the country road, sat a large black van.

Frosell cursed beneath his breath, not quite loud enough for his wife or the bewildered Heddy to hear the exact words, but they certainly caught the sentiment. Frosell had no doubt the D.G.E.R. had the van waiting in the dark all along and had used the headlights of their impressive convoy of cars to flush him out of the villa. The mysterious telephone call had most likely been of their making too—all part of their tactic to get Oscar Frosell precisely where they wanted him.

There was nowhere to go. The driveway was too narrow to turn the car around quickly, and even if he did attempt to reverse all the way back to the villa, then what?

The Dauphine's door was yanked open and a flashlight shone directly into Frosell's eyes.

"Who is it, father?" Heddy appeared between the seats. She rubbed at her sleepy eyes and, thankfully, appeared none the worse for her rude awakening.

"It's okay; stay back." With one hand, Frosell shielded his eyes against the piercing light.

"You're coming with us, *collaborateur*," the voice behind the light hissed. Then, a strong hand grabbed Frosell's arm and pulled him roughly from the car and out onto the cold gravel of the driveway.

"Oscar!" Marie's shrill, terrified voice rang out in the night as more lights arrived to shine through the car's windows and blind her with their glare.

More hands grabbed at Frosell and he was hoisted to his feet. He struggled against their grip and protested, "There's no need for this." He attempted to wrench his arms free. "My lawyer has been notified—" A swift, hard punch to the stomach silenced Frosell. He bent double, gasping for breath and holding onto the side of the car for support.

"Take the traitor away!" a voice snapped, and Frosell found himself being physically dragged away from his family. Somewhere ahead of him, amid the blaze of headlights filling the lane, Frosell heard the word *Gestapo*, among others even less pleasant, and he hoped his wife and daughter couldn't hear them.

Heddy looked on in horror and cried out for her father as she watched the bad men carry him away. She scrabbled over to the front seat where her mother held her tight and whispered soothing noises, even though Marie was as terrified as her little girl.

There was nothing Marie could do. For as much as she wanted to chase after her husband, get him back to the car, and flee, she knew it was a futile idea; the family was literally surrounded by dozens of black-clad D.G.E.R. agents—most likely all of them armed—and she couldn't leave Heddy. As the brightness of the flashlight beams pinned her inside the car, Marie cried with her daughter and wondered when she'd see her husband again.

CHAPTER SIXTEEN

Saint-Cloud, France. May 18ᵗʰ, 1945.

The ordeal was all beginning to take its toll on her husband; Marie would have to have been blind not to have seen the changes in Oscar since the day of his voluntary meeting with Lieutenant Avot and subsequent arrest. Of course, he was still the strong, intimidating man she had married what seemed like a lifetime ago, and he still carried himself with dignity and character, but the changes were subtle, perhaps so subtle only a loving wife could see them, and she could tell his health was beginning to suffer.

The smoking was a constant, of course, although Marie thought it had actually increased over the months; it was ever more rare to find Oscar without his precious onyx cigarette holder pressed between his lips. His complexion had taken on the slightest tinge of gray, and his eyes had lost enough of their fierce sparkle to cause Marie concern. Oscar even had a hint of a stoop to his stature now, as if the burden of the previous year and the fight for restitution were physically weighing his broad, powerful shoulders down. But, all the more worrying for Marie was her husband's manic obsession with

153

the catalog of injustices that had been forced upon his family; they occupied his every waking moment, and much of his dreams, too. Oscar would often mutter names out loud in his sleep, and sometimes he'd dictate legal letters to his long-suffering lawyer as he slept.

Family dinners had become a rare event too, as Marie and Heddy would more often eat alone while Oscar busied himself in his study preparing arguments and pressing Dzeroginsky—who had become almost as regular a sight at the villa as Heddy's tutor—for more information and pushing him to file yet more litigation.

Marie knew in her heart that, for as strong as her husband was, not even one with the strongest constitution could possibly keep up with the stress Oscar had put himself under. She also knew that, along with the persistent intimidation from the French and Sweden's inaction, sooner or later, something was going to give.

Josef Dzeroginsky was at the house again. Once more, he was in conference with her husband in the lounge. He'd most likely be staying for dinner—Marie's lamb casserole was one of the lawyer's favorites—which at least meant Marie and Heddy would get some semblance of a family meal, even though most of the conversation would invariably revolve around talk of the restoration of the Frosell fortune.

"Must we go through all this again?" Frosell sighed. He lit a cigarette with the dying embers of the stub in his holder, swapped the two out, and took a deep draw.

Dzeroginsky nodded. "If we are to correctly present the facts to the state, then yes," he said.

"It was a farce, just like the arrest before it," Frosell grunted through a plume of smoke. "They dragged me away in the middle of the night, and I returned home on the 15ᵗʰ March with no charges to answer; they barely had time to process me."

Dzeroginsky jotted on his notepad; he knew the date of his client's midnight arrest and consequent release two days later by heart. Frosell had disturbed the lawyer's sleep that night and he'd had to drive him home to the villa; the D.G.E.R. were not good at returning people they'd snatched in front of their families in the middle of the night. "Are you sure they didn't advise you any reasons for your arrest?"

Frosell snorted and eyed the lawyer. For as much as he'd grown to consider the man a friend, his doggedness could be quite infuriating. "When they transferred me to the Civil Police Special Branch on the 13ᵗʰ, I asked on many occasions throughout my brief stay in their cells, and no one offered any explanation at all. Even when Commissioner Guerin had no choice but to sign my release, as there were no grounds for the charges brought against me, nobody cared to tell me what those charges were, nor who had brought them against me." He sucked angrily on his cigarette and inhaled deeply. "Although they did show far more fairness than the D.G.E.R.; they even requested the dossier when I told them the military police had ruled in my favor."

"And yet, mysteriously, that dossier didn't materialize," Dzeroginsky mumbled as he scribbled his notes—more for his own benefit than his client's.

"They held me for two days while the D.G.E.R. searched for it—ostensibly, at least." Frosell's words were illustrated by puffs of smoke. "All of the original Secret Police documents about my case appear to have simply vanished into thin air, Josef." He leaned forward and pinched the bridge of his nose between forefinger and thumb, as if trying to hold back a particularly severe migraine. "And along with them, any proof of my innocence in all of this."

"I have obtained three other legal advisors to collate the material again and gather new evidence for our next legal battle. Are you sure you're up to it, Oscar?" Dzeroginsky addressed him as a concerned friend.

"Of course I am." Frosell appeared a tad offended by his lawyer's inference he hadn't the fortitude to go into battle with the state. "My enemies are not going to give up that easily, Josef." He fixed Dzeroginsky with an icy glare. "And for as long as I'm alive and a free man in France, they'll keep coming for me; even if I give up my fight for what rightfully belongs to my family, I fear they will be relentless and will not stop until I flee the county like a coward or I'm . . ."

The unspoken work hung in the air as thick and tangible as the smoke from Frosell's cigarettes.

"I really don't think it will come to that." It was Dzeroginsky who broke the loaded silence. "Once we have all the information back together, along with Nordling's retraction of his earlier statement regarding your citizenship and the judgment against the Dumesnils, I believe we have an incredibly strong case to claim compensation from the French." He quit making notes to look his client square in the eyes. "Although, as your lawyer and friend, I would advise you to leave the country once we file. You are going to make some seriously important enemies here in France."

"Thank you for the advice, Monsieur Dzeroginsky." The slightest hint of a smile crinkled the corners of Frosell's mouth. "Now, let's eat. Marie's lamb smells exceptionally delicious this evening, don't you think?"

Heddy was out playing in the warm spring sunshine when, only two days later, the bad men came for her father again.

She wore her favorite smock dress—as yellow as the fresh spring daffodils—and the oversized matching bow Mother always insisted putting in her hair. The bow was less of a favorite with Heddy, as it was uncomfortable and bulky. But, it made her mother smile to see her little girl wearing it, and that had to be worth any amount of discomfort.

Only two black cars turned up that morning, which was far less terrifying than the procession of sinister vehicles that had ambushed them two months before. One of the policemen even smiled at Heddy as he and three others made their way to the villa's front door to call for her father, and then smiled again as they escorted him to one of their cars.

All thoughts of her game evaporated as Heddy rushed to comfort her mother, who stood in the doorway and watched as her husband was taken away for the fourth time. Marie shed no tears this time, as she had grown hardened to the routine—Oscar had even preempted this supposed surprise visit by the Secret Police and had warned her the moment Dzeroginsky filed once more for restitution. The state's intimidation of Oscar Frosell was becoming so predictable, it would have been comical had it not meant watching her husband being driven away yet again.

And, although he would be released without charge the very next day, neither Heddy nor her mother was to know that as they took him away; all they could do was hope for the best as they feared for the worst.

CHAPTER SEVENTEEN

Law Offices of Josef Dzeroginsky, Rue de Cygne, Paris.
September 13th, 1945.

"You look like hell, Oscar." The lawyer peered at his client across the desk. "Are you sleeping at all?"

Frosell lit a cigarette—his fifth in the short span of their meeting that morning. "Thanks a lot, Josef. Aren't you supposed to make me feel better?" He managed a cynical smile. "And I'm sleeping just fine, thank you," he lied. He sucked hard on the cigarette and drew the smoke deep into his body before expelling it with a wheezing, hacking cough, which reminded him of the consumption victims he'd encountered as a small boy.

"None of this is doing you any good at all," Dzeroginsky persisted. "Or Marie and Heddy, for that matter. Have you stopped to consider how your . . . obsession is affecting them?"

"Of course," Frosell replied. "I am doing it for them as much as myself, you know that."

"You barely acknowledge either one of them these days, Oscar." Dzeroginsky was genuinely concerned—he considered the Frosells to be good friends and regarded the family as fondly as he did his own. Watching firsthand Frosell's consuming fixation with his seemingly hopeless fight against France was difficult for the lawyer; it was, quite literally, sucking the life out of Oscar Frosell and his poor family. "Perhaps it *would* be wise for you to consider splitting your money with the state? After all, even half of the Frosell fortune is more money than any one person could even hope to spend in a lifetime."

"Josef"—cigarette holder clamped between his teeth, Frosell leaned forward in his chair and frowned—"you are my lawyer, not my doctor. I see you as a friend, and I do value our friendship, but when it comes to business, I need you to stick to the matter at hand. I'd like to get this meeting over so I can get home and celebrate my wife's birthday with her. She was feeling odd this morning, somewhat worried when I left. And besides, I think it is a little too late for me to be entering into any kind of deal with the French government."

Dzeroginsky sighed. "I understand, Oscar, but there is a possible end to all of this—one that does not involve the complete ruination of you and your family."

"I have a judgment in my favor, Josef," Frosell insisted. "How the Dumesnils went about commandeering my apartment and plundering my property was unlawful; we have that much in black and white." He puffed out a thick plume of smoke, which hung above his head like a storm cloud.

"But the judgment absolved the state of all responsibility," Dzeroginsky countered. "It clearly states Major Dumesnil was acting as a civilian when she and her associates requisitioned 6 Rue

Dufrenoy, and therefore the state carries no liability. And let's not forget the general's role in all of this."

Frosell stared hard at the lawyer; sometimes it could be very hard to like the man, especially when he played devil's advocate. "De Gaulle signed the order as a favor to Girardot and Major Dumesnil. That much has to be irrefutable."

"But who will stand against the man who liberated France? De Gaulle is a national—*international*—hero, Oscar, and as such is seen as being above reproach."

"All we have to do is show that Alla Dumesnil was acting within her position as a major of the air force and we win. And, given General Bouscat himself signed the first requisition order, it really shouldn't be all that difficult."

The lawyer shook his head. No, in theory, it shouldn't have been all that difficult. But, when one factored in the quite deliberate use of "madame" instead of "major" on the judgment, the question mark still hanging over Frosell's alleged collaboration and wartime profiteering, *and* the not so minor point that General de Gaulle was involved, the whole case was built on increasingly shifting sands.

Continuing, Frosell said, "I need you to file another request for restitution."

"Another?"

"Another." A puff of smoke. "We have to keep applying pressure, Josef; hold their attention and make people aware of the travesty of justice my family has suffered at the hands of the French government."

"I fear we have already attracted the attention of the wrong people." Dzeroginsky ran a hand through his rapidly thinning hair. "Which is why you have been incarcerated four times. Is that not enough, Oscar?"

It was Frosell's turn to shake his head. "The French can throw me in whatever jail they want, Josef, but they won't break me. And I'm not going to quit until justice has been served and I'm given back what the state has taken from me—every damn cent of it."

Dzeroginsky offered Frosell a smile. "I am here to advise you, as well as act as you instruct; if you choose to ignore my advice, then that is your business, Oscar." He reached for a pen and a fresh wad of paper. "I shall get started on the new filing immediately."

As Frosell thanked him and made to leave, the lawyer thought he looked somehow smaller than on the occasion of their first meeting. Frosell was still an intimidating man in stature and character, but something about the forward slouch of his shoulders and the haunted look that had settled across his face made him seem less than he had been all those months ago. Josef Dzeroginsky let out a weary sigh as he watched Frosell leave his office; he knew, more than many, what it was to face injustice and lose everything.

Rue de Cygne was sunny and warm when Oscar Frosell stepped out from his lawyer's dour offices. Fall was getting well underway; the harshness had been sapped from the sun's heat, and the trees were making their annual transformation from rich greens to the burnt coppers and reds of the season. Frosell set aside his cigarette for a moment and drew in a deep breath of the wonderful air—it tasted fresh and clean and carried with it the heady scents of a city on the cusp of a new era. And for a moment, Frosell believed he could—*would*—win recompense from the country that had so wronged him, justice would prevail, and he and his wife and daughter would live out their lives happy and without a care in the world.

It was to be the last time Oscar Frosell would taste freedom for over two years.

Screeching to a halt, the Black Maria mounted the sidewalk in front of him. Before Frosell had time to process or react, three black-clad men jumped out, grabbed him, and wrestled him to the ground like some common criminal. As Frosell went down hard, his onyx cigarette holder fell from his hand and snapped in two against the paving slabs. "Stop!" Frosell gasped as he was roughly manhandled up off the ground and toward the van. "I demand to see my lawyer!"

"There'll be plenty of time for that, *collaborateur*," a voice snarled in his ear. Frosell's arms were twisted roughly behind his back, and he felt the familiar cold metal bite of handcuffs as they were snapped around his wrists.

"In." Another voice gave Frosell no choice but to clamber into the vehicle.

"Where are you taking me?" Frosell was determined to maintain control of his panic; no way was he going to beg and plead with these people, nor would there be any point in doing so. They were there to do their job, under orders to collect one Oscar Frosell from the street outside his lawyer's office. Frosell's beef would be with whoever had given those orders—although at that point, it could well have been any number of people.

"You'll find out soon enough, *Gestapo*," the first voice growled in Frosell's ear as a powerful, meaty hand gave him a resolute shove toward the back of the van.

Frosell fell forward onto harsh, chill metal. Without hands to break the fall, his head rattled hard and an overwhelming dizziness washed through his mind. Determined to keep his wits about him, Frosell willed himself not to pass out, and he conjured happy thoughts of Marie and Heddy and tried not to think about what his further incarceration would do to them. He hoped this time would be as transitory as his previous excursions to the D.G.E.R., but somehow this felt altogether different. They had snatched him from directly outside Dzeroginsky's office, which showed a complete disregard for his civil rights, and the lawyer had observed them doing so.

Nothing about it boded well at all for Oscar Frosell.

CHAPTER EIGHTEEN

D.G.E.R. prison, Boulevard Suchet, Paris.
September 14th, 1945.

A mere twelve days after the Japanese officially surrendered on the USS Missouri, moored in Tokyo Bay, which heralded the true end of the world war, Oscar Frosell was summoned to face yet another hastily assembled court that had no real charges against him.

They had allowed Dzeroginsky to attend the procedure—to have called it a hearing would have been to bestow upon it some semblance of justice, and Frosell was not about to let that happen—which came as a surprise. Although, as the farce continued, it became increasingly clear the presence of Frosell's lawyer was nothing more than for show; the verdict was a foregone conclusion right from the start.

Nordling was there, and although he kept his bulky frame and hard face hidden at the back of the makeshift courtroom, as far as Frosell was concerned, the man's presence hung over the place like some malevolent spirit. Had it not been for the general consul's deliberate indiscretion at the behest of Admiral Dumesnil, Frosell doubted any of this travesty of French justice would be happening.

"The arrest warrant was granted by the investigating judge of the Seine Court of Justice, Monsieur Pierre Duval," the presiding judge of the kangaroo court—Monsieur Gilbert Laurent, a crusty old general with dubious legal qualifications—answered Dzeroginsky's question. "For the crimes of collaboration and profiteering during wartime."

"All of those accusations have already been answered." Dzeroginsky remained firm. "Along with the wholly untrue allegations of my client not being a Swedish citizen and of being a German citizen and Gestapo agent. All of these have been proven to be nothing more than fabrications to detract from the violations against Monsieur Frosell and his family, and the looting of his personal property. The plundering has been sanctioned by the state and is in direct violation of the superior orders my client had in place to protect his personal property and belongings."

"These are serious allegations, Monsieur Dzeroginsky," Laurent replied with a scowl. "I suggest you choose your words carefully."

"All are well documented and refuted," Dzeroginsky replied coldly. "You have the documents. You know the facts, Your Honor."

"We are here to look for grounds for an indictment," Laurent said with smug self-satisfaction. "And in the meantime, to decide what to do with Monsieur Frosell."

The lawyer looked across the gray stone room at Frosell, who sat bolt upright in his uncomfortable metal chair, head held high and eyes fixed firmly upon Monsieur Laurent; yet for the confident, defiant façade he presented, Dzeroginsky thought Oscar Frosell appeared to be even less well than he had the day before in his office. "My client has a letter from the Royal Swedish Embassy here in Paris protesting his innocence. They are offering a bail of five million francs, the surrender of Monsieur Frosell's passport, and their guarantee of release on bail due to his general ill health." There was also the complete absence of any incriminating evidence, guilt, or motive, and the fact that Oscar Frosell was a well-respected, married family man and legal Paris resident with a legitimate residence, but Dzeroginsky knew Laurent already knew all of that and didn't much care. The man's orders had obviously come from high above—perhaps even as high as it was possible to get—and all of this was a mere formality.

"I'm afraid Monsieur Frosell is too likely to flee the country," Laurent countered. "Especially since he no longer has access to his family residence." Frosell flinched at the comment, and his lawyer thought for a split second he was about to shout the judge down. But no, Frosell maintained his stoicism and dignity. "Therefore, I am sending him to Fresnes prison until such a time as grounds for indictment can be found." In other words, until they dug up something—or fabricated evidence—they would incarcerate a man who had been proven innocent on more than one occasion.

"I must object to that," Dzeroginsky said. "My client is not a well man; such imprisonment will only exacerbate his poor health."

"The decision has been made." Laurent looked around on his small metal table, as if searching for a gavel. There were only scattered papers and an old ink pen. "That will be all."

Dzeroginsky sat down heavily, and his own small metal chair groaned beneath his weight. Fresnes was perhaps the worst place they could possibly have condemned Frosell to—the place was nothing more than a concentration camp, which had gained in notoriety since the end of the war. Also, and of major concern, Frosell's imprisonment there was indicative of interference by the *Police Judiciaire*—known and feared as simply the P.J. They were, ironically, given the nature of the accusations leveled at Frosell, the French equivalent of the German Gestapo; any order to appear before them at Fresnes was considered by many to be the equivalent of certain death.

"Don't blame yourself, Josef," Frosell whispered. "This was a done deal even before they kidnapped me from the street yesterday. Most likely it was planned when they realized they couldn't keep holding me at Boulevard Suchet without charge. Even the corrupt French government has its limits—especially in the face of so much international scrutiny."

"That was all nothing more than bullying, Oscar," Dzeroginsky said with a weary sigh. "They wanted you to take their deal or back off completely—maybe even go back to Sweden and forget any of this ever happened. The only reason they've not had you killed thus far is because that's one thing guaranteed to have the Swedish up in arms *and* alert the rest of Europe to de Gaulle's duplicity. You are by no means the only wealthy foreigner this is happening to; anything less and your country will be only too happy to keep out of it to maintain their neutrality."

A pair of thickset, surly D.G.E.R. agents approached Frosell and his lawyer. Behind them lurked a sinister quartet of soldiers, their guns held at hip height, fingers poised on triggers. "Come," one of the agents grunted at Frosell.

"My client is in counsel," Dzeroginsky protested.

"Court is adjourned," Monsieur Laurent barked from across the room; he was busy stacking his papers into a neat pile, all ready to leave. "Sentence has been passed. Your client is to be transported to Fresnes immediately. You will, of course, be permitted to visit with him at the prison."

Dzeroginsky could only begin to imagine how difficult they were going to make any form of visitation. He considered asking Monsieur Laurent about a motion to appeal but dismissed it as folly, since the judge of the farcical proceedings had been nothing more than a puppet for the state.

"Tell Marie not to worry," Frosell said as the agents and soldiers ushered him toward the door. They handcuffed his hands tight behind his back, as if determined to rob the man of any last remaining grain of dignity. "And Heddy too—tell her I said I'll write and she is to take good care of her mother."

"Come on," one of the agents growled, and the harshness of his voice resounded about the grim walls of the room. He gave Frosell a shove in the small of his back, which caused him to stumble through the door and out into the hallway beyond.

The lawyer watched as his client, his *friend*, was frog marched away until he was out of sight. He had a dull, sinking feeling in the pit of his stomach. Although he'd seen Oscar Frosell incarcerated four times before—sometimes on the same flimsy, fabricated charges, and other times with not even that much of an excuse—this time seemed different. There'd been the façade of a trial on the order of Monsieur Pierre Duval, the complete disregard of the Swedish Embassy, the sentence of incarceration at the infamous Fresnes camp—even the fact they'd invited Frosell's lawyer along, ostensibly to ensure justice was served; none of it boded well in his book. And, even though he was not prone to bouts of pessimism, Dzeroginsky couldn't shake the terrible feeling not only would Frosell not be released within a day or two as before, but also that he may not be leaving Fresnes at all.

Law Offices of Josef Dzeroginsky, Rue de Cygne, Paris.

The minute Marie Frosell learned from Dzeroginsky that not only was her husband not going to be released from the D.G.E.R prison as she had been led to expect, but that he was to be shipped off to Fresnes Jail, she mobilized herself and made her way to Boulevard Suchet the next day. The lawyer, ever the one to advise she exercise caution in such matters, had told her they were highly unlikely to allow her to visit with Frosell and that her actions may well make things worse for him.

"How could things possibly be any worse for Oscar, Josef?" Marie had raised her voice to the lawyer, even though he was merely the messenger, which had startled Heddy, who sat making up her stories within earshot. "They already have him in prison under the most ridiculous, made-up charges, and now they intend to ship him off to somewhere even worse, and farther away from me and Heddy!"

Heddy's ears pricked up at the sound of her name spoken at such high volume; the only other times she heard it spoken like that were whenever she was in trouble. And, while she was pleased her mother's wrath was not directed at her, it upset Heddy to hear the anger and fear in her voice.

"I wish you'd allow me to deal with this," Dzeroginsky protested. "You don't know what it's like dealing with these people. Harassing them is going to be counterproductive, Marie."

"It worked with them the last time, Josef," Marie snapped back. "If I can get them to allow me to see Oscar, or at least persuade them to keep him at Boulevard Suchet rather than Fresnes, I would be happy—for now."

"That's highly unlikely to happen." The lawyer kept his voice calm and even; he was as accustomed to Marie's stubbornness as he was to her energy and passion.

"Which one?" Marie demanded.

"Any of them—I think you already know that." Dzeroginsky sighed and sat himself down. He cast a quick glance at Heddy, who smiled back at him; she sat quietly, patiently in the tiny waiting room of his office, her little imagination transporting her away from the grim reality of the lawyer's office and off to far-flung lands populated by characters she'd invented to keep her company. But, she kept one ear tuned to her mother's heated exchange with the lawyer who was becoming like one of the family; the little girl had a sinking feeling in the pit of her stomach what was coming next.

"If I don't try, how could I know that?" Marie was up on her feet and reaching for her coat. "You tried your way, Josef, and you failed. You let the D.G.E.R do whatever they like with my husband."

Dzeroginsky recoiled as if Marie had slapped him in the face. He looked across at Heddy again, as if concerned she might catch him looking embarrassed. Heddy, however, was immersed in her own little world and didn't as much as look over at him. "I have done everything within my power to assist Oscar—you know that. The D.G.E.R are operating under a far higher power than any lawyer could hope to go up against under such circumstances. De Gaulle and his government are practically untouchable right now, and the Swedes are burying their heads in the sand to avoid the whole situation as best they can."

"Then what are we paying you for?" Marie stuck an arm into her coat sleeve with purpose.

"I will make progress, Marie," Dzeroginsky defended. "It just all takes time, that's all."

"I fear my husband may not have the luxury of time." Marie buttoned up her coat and nodded at Heddy to make herself ready to leave. "He is not well suited to incarceration, Josef. You've seen for yourself how it's affecting his health."

The lawyer could only agree. "I fully understand Oscar's predic-ament," he said. "I have advised him of the best course of action—"

"You advised him to run away to Sweden!" Marie grabbed her purse from Dzeroginsky's desk. "And you know full well Oscar would never, ever do that. He has never run away from a fight in his life, Josef."

"Perhaps he should learn to accept when he is beaten?"

"While ever my husband has right on his side and there's breath in his body, he'll fight with everything he's got." Marie made her way to the door, where Heddy waited with her coat buttoned all the way to the top and a forced smile on her face. "And I'm going to fight right there alongside him, Josef. I'm sure you'd expect nothing less."

"Of course." The lawyer forced a smile.

"I'm not leaving Paris until I've done everything within my power to help Oscar." With that, Marie headed out of the lawyer's dull, gray office with Heddy in tow.

True to her word, Marie arrived outside the D.G.E.R. prison after a short bus ride from Rue de Cygne, which dropped her and Heddy off at the opposite end of Boulevard Suchet.

Heddy stuck close to the tails of her mother's coat; the prison was a terrifying place for someone so small, even though they had made it no farther in than the front office.

"I demand to see my husband!" Marie's voice sounded dampened in the small space.

"Hello again, Madame Frosell." The officer behind the desk greeted Marie as he might an old friend. "I'm afraid I cannot sanction that outside of normal visiting hours."

"Then call someone who can sanction it!" Marie pointed at a sorry-looking pair of rickety old wooden chairs and gave Heddy a gentle nudge toward them. Obediently, and without a flicker of protest, Heddy scuttled across the stone floor and perched herself up on one of the chairs; she knew the routine well enough and, within seconds, was off in her own world once more.

"I'm not leaving until I see either my husband or someone who will put a stop to the ridiculous plan to move him to Fresnes." Marie stood her ground, arms folded across her chest.

"I'm sorry, madame, but your haranguing is not going to do you any good, not today." The officer looked quite apologetic. "We have orders from above, which we have no choice but to stick to. You will be able to see Monsieur Frosell once he is transported to Fresnes; I'm sure there will be buses that will take you there."

"You are missing my point, monsieur." Marie spat the last word like it was poison on her tongue. "I do not want him to be taken to Fresnes. He deserves to be released, not moved, since he has done absolutely nothing wrong!" Marie's raised voice caught the attention of the officer's colleagues. Heads turned, all eyes on the irate woman at the front desk.

Slowly, the officer shook his head. "I am very sorry, Madame Frosell, but it is already done; your husband is already on his way to Fresnes."

Heddy caught sight of her mother's face and the look of abject desperation that settled there. Hopping down from her wobbly old chair, she scurried across to wrap her arms about Mother's legs.

Heddy wished she could have offered more. She wished she were big and fearsome enough to tower over the stupid prison officer in his stupid uniform and force him to let her father go.

CHAPTER NINETEEN

Saint-Cloud, France. October 17th, 1945.

Over a month had gone by since Josef Dzeroginsky had made the tearfully apologetic telephone call to Marie regarding her husband's rushed trial and subsequent incarceration at Fresnes, and still she had not been permitted to see him. It was not as if the lawyer hadn't tried his best; he had called the jail daily, petitioned in writing to allow Frosell the basic human right of seeing his wife and child, and had even gone so far as to write to the Swedish consulate to ask them to add their diplomatic weight. So far their silence had been deafening.

Marie had reassured Dzeroginsky it was not his fault, and she in no way held him accountable. From what Oscar had divulged to her previously, the whole case was far bigger than even one of the best lawyers in Paris could handle. The corruption that had allowed the French state to plunder the Frosells' fortune and render the family homeless stretched all the way to the top, and Marie's husband seemed to be little more than a nuisance they were having trouble disposing of.

Marie had spoken to Dzeroginsky earlier in the day, and he'd had nothing new to tell her. There was no news of Oscar and absolutely nothing of the numerous appeals the lawyer had lodged to free him from Fresnes. And, of course, they received no news of possible visits—for either Dzeroginsky or Marie and Heddy. Marie had the impression the lawyer's weekly phone calls were more of a friendly check-in to ensure his client's family was holding body and soul together. Some days it felt a little too much like charity, but Marie appreciated at least that one tenuous link to her beloved husband.

Heddy trotted over from playing. "Will Father be coming home soon?" she asked. She had been playing in the living room, where she'd taken it over with an elaborate construction of the furniture, cushions, and bed sheets. Some days it was a castle, others a fort, but today it was a train. Heddy would play in there for hours on end, along with the stray kitten who had adopted her and Marie as its new family; it had simply wandered in one morning, mewling and looking most pitiful. Heddy had named him Arthur, and he followed her around more like a puppy than a cat. She would dress him in small, makeshift clothes, bathe him, and put him to bed like a baby. He was her one true friend in Saint-Cloud and a welcome distraction from the turmoil that was rocking her family.

"Will he be home for Christmas again?" Heddy said, and it took all of Marie's resolve to hold back her tears. From the day they'd returned from vacationing in Cosne-Cours—only fourteen short months ago that now felt like an eternity—to be told by their supposedly well-meaning friends they must flee for their lives, Marie had done her utmost to remain strong for both her husband and daughter. She had listened with patience to Oscar's increasingly wild rants about how the Dumesnils, the French, the Swedish consul, and even de Gaulle himself had conspired to swindle the Frosell family and commit state-sanctioned plundering of everything they owned, and she had maintained a courageous pretense for Heddy each time her father had been taken away. The child was a most precocious six-year-old now and had a good grasp of what was going on, all thanks to her penchant for listening in to her father's conversations with both Marie and his lawyer.

And now, a month after Oscar had been snatched from the street, the stress of their circumstances was taking its toll on Marie, and she felt herself teetering on the edge of a complete breakdown. She would jump each time she heard a noise outside, imagine knocks on the door that always turned out to be phantom, and she couldn't remember the last time she'd had an unbroken night's sleep. Every night since Oscar was taken away, she would awake around three in the morning—the devil's hour, some called it—and she'd lie in the big, empty bed until the dawn chorus and try not to imagine what her dear husband was going through in that dreadful prison. She'd also play in her mind what she would say to Heddy should Dzeroginsky call one day with the terrible news she'd been dreading since her husband's first incarceration.

Sometimes Marie would forget to eat, especially on the days she spent at the consulate and the Paris law courts campaigning for her husband's release. Marie had become almost as single-minded as her husband, and she struck terror into the hearts of the bureaucrats who had the misfortune to get in her way. If she prepared a meal only for Heddy and not the both of them, she would often fall exhausted into bed only for her empty, growling stomach to awaken her even earlier than the customary three a.m. She could tell from the way her favorite dresses hung loose on her slender frame that she was losing weight, and had even gone so far as to take a few of them in rather than force herself to eat against the leaden feeling of nausea that never seemed to leave her stomach.

"I'm hoping so, Heddy," Marie placated her daughter, although she didn't dare get either of their hopes up.

"Did Monsieur Dzeroginsky tell you he was going to get Father out of jail again?"

"Something like that, dear." Absently, Marie toyed with the huge yellow bow that hung limp in her daughter's hair. "I'm sure it won't be much longer now." She fought back the ever-present threat of tears and hoped against hope Heddy wouldn't pick up on the doubt that laced her voice.

But Heddy was content in her own little world; she'd lose herself within her vivid imagination and often seemed oblivious to her mother's more frequent depressed moods. The little girl found delight in the smallest pleasures life had to offer, especially when she tagged along with Marie on one of her trips into Paris to raise hell with the authorities over her husband's appalling treatment or to seek out what food she could in the sparsely stocked stores around the city.

On one such occasion, Heddy and her mother had been approached by an American soldier; he'd been walking by, minding his own business when Heddy had said hello. Allied soldiers were commonplace in the days and months after the end of the war, and Heddy had come to see them as welcome, friendly faces after the suffocating oppression of the Nazi occupation she'd lived through.

The soldier seemed delighted to have been waylaid by such a sweet, precocious young lady, and asked Marie's permission to present Heddy with a candy bar. Of course, there was no way any mother could possibly have refused back then, as sweet treats were so scarce. The candy bar she enjoyed, which was similar to the Payday bars Heddy would love later on in her life, was the first time she had eaten peanuts; bars like that simply did not exist in France, as they were an American import.

Whether due to the kindness of the soldier, the happy memory of that day with her beloved mother, or merely the wonderful taste of the candy itself, that first bite of the nut-covered candy bar was to mark the beginning of Heddy's lifelong love affair with Payday bars, even though she was accustomed to the finest chocolates from around the world that she used to purloin from the exquisite boxes her mother adored.

CHAPTER TWENTY

Fresnes Jail, Fresnes, Val-de-Marne. November 5ᵗʰ, 1947.

Home for Oscar Frosell was a foreboding two-story gray stone building with a tall, imposing double front gate. It sat twenty miles south of Paris, was comprised of twelve hundred cells, and housed over triple that number of prisoners—many of them political and alleged Nazi collaborators who were held with little evidence more than hearsay and accusations.

He knew the P.J. held influence over the jail, and they used it not only to contain those they considered enemies of the state, but as a place in which they could obtain confessions by any means they deemed necessary, and with complete impunity.

Frosell refused to allow Fresnes' appalling culture of abuse and brutality to break him—no matter how hard they tried. Although he'd spent the first six months or so of his incarceration in a dark, cramped cell with three other prisoners, he'd still been able to create drawings, fancy cards, and little wooden boxes with inlaid silver thread for Heddy; it saddened him to realize he had no way of knowing when she'd get to see them. When they'd arrested him, Frosell had assumed his latest, contrived imprisonment would be much the same as the others and he'd be home again in little more than a couple of days, a week at the most.

But here he was, two long, lonely years later.

But then, with no explanation, they'd moved Frosell into the prison's lower solitary cells, which were reserved for hardened criminals and those who were to be prepared for interrogation. Once secured within the dank bowels of Fresnes, the soldiers had subjected Frosell to sleep deprivation, psychological torture, and the ever-constant threat of execution. A good number of the soldiers who worked as guards at Fresnes were unstable—and drunk for much of the time—and well-practiced and most zealous in the brutal interrogation techniques they'd learned during the war.

"Wake up, *collaborateur*!" The cold, hard steel of a machine gun's muzzle dug deep into Frosell's ribs. "*Now!*" The rough woolen blanket was ripped away, and the harsh chill of the early morning air gnawed at Frosell's joints.

With no time to complain and no choice but to obey, Frosell heaved his stiff, weary body off the concrete slab and straw-filled mattress serving as his bed and stumbled to his feet. The soldier jabbed the gun between Frosell's shoulder blades and, automatically, he put his hands behind his back to invite the inevitable bite of steel handcuffs.

It was the second time in the space of less than a week the soldiers had rounded him up for cross-examination at five a.m., and the sixth time in what Frosell estimated to be a month—time had gradually lost all meaning in the absence of daylight. In all, he'd been subjected to this same demeaning routine 176 times during his stay at Fresnes.

One of the three soldiers snapped handcuffs on Frosell's wrists, and then they frog marched him from the cell and out into the freezing cold of the prison courtyard. There, he was bundled into the same Black Maria van that awaited him each and every time.

Huddled in a corner of the van, Frosell chose to remain silent. He'd learned the hard way early on that the best option was not to try to engage the soldiers; they knew where he was going and what for, and had no desire to speak with a traitor and enemy of the people. During his early days at Fresnes, Frosell had tried to speak to his captors, only to receive vile insults and violence in return.

The trip in the van was short, mercifully so, and Frosell wondered once more why the trip couldn't have been taken by foot; most likely it was all part of the lengthy process to disorient him prior to interrogation. The van jerked to a stop, and Frosell was hauled out. The soldiers ushered him into what had been designated the Fresnes prison court building. There, sometime later, the day's examining judge would take residence, and Frosell would be put before him for yet another farcical and wholly contrived cross-examination.

"Make yourself at home," one of the soldiers sneered. He pulled open the door to the all-too-familiar basement cell and gave Frosell a hearty shove in the back with his fist.

Frosell staggered forward and almost fell. "Don't get too comfortable, *Gestapo*." The guard spat at Frosell's feet and slammed the metal door shut with a resounding *clang*.

The dark, dank cell was constructed of dark stone and measured little more than six feet by six feet; it was illuminated by a single bare light bulb that barely filled the claustrophobic space with weak, jaundiced light. There was, as was usual, not so much as a stool or a proper latrine—just an old iron bucket in one corner, which was totally impossible for Frosell to use with his hands cuffed behind his back. There was nothing to sit on, except for the cold stone floor, and he would get no food or water; sometimes they'd make him go without food for three whole days prior to interrogation. Frosell had learned from bitter experience not to expect any sustenance, just as he knew there was little point asking the soldiers for any, as the entire reason for locking him up in that dreadful, inhumane place for six, seven, sometimes eight or nine hours at a time was to soften him up in an attempt to make him all the more pliable for the judge's questioning. He'd overheard the soldiers refer to the whole sorry process as *grilling*, but in reality, it was nothing more than torture. With a heavy sigh, Frosell leaned his back against the wall and managed to lower himself down to sit on the floor.

All he could do now was wait.

It was well past midafternoon when the soldiers finally came for him. He'd managed to doze a little; his body and mind had grown so weary, he could easily have fallen asleep anywhere. The cruel soldiers took great delight in kicking at their prisoner's legs to awaken him.

"The judge is ready for you, Gestapo." The soldiers watched as Frosell struggled to his feet. Not one of them offered to help. Instead, they each prodded at him with their guns. Of course, Frosell was well used to the routine and knew the route like the back of his hand. Slowly, he made his way along the hallway, up the stone stairs, and into the makeshift courtroom.

"Oscar Frosell," the judge offered by means of a formal greeting, "you are accused of collaboration and of being a Gestapo agent." Frosell sighed and nodded his head; the judge was the only component unfamiliar to Frosell—he'd been through the exact same process and contradictory questions what felt like a thousand times. And each time, he'd remained steadfast in his replies, no matter how many times thinly veiled threats were aimed at him and his family. Even as the Fresnes regime weakened him physically and mentally, Oscar Frosell continued to protest his innocence with vehemence, accuse those who had executed the official plundering of his family's possessions, and refuse to allow himself to be broken.

"I plead not guilty to all charges, Your Honor." The last word stuck in Frosell's throat—honor was one thing definitely lacking in both the judge and the farcical court.

The judge peered at Frosell over his wire-framed, pince-nez spectacles. "There is the matter of the testimony of one Salvator Delaplace to be addressed." He read slowly from the papers stacked before him, as if reading were a mystery to him. "He swore on oath you were a colonel in the German S.S."

Frosell stared with contempt at the man; he was no more a qualified judge than any of the gun-toting, alcohol-soaked soldiers who stood sentry around the courtroom. Of course, the authorities had not allowed Frosell any form of representation in any of the proceedings

at Fresnes, so he'd not so much as set eyes on Dzeroginsky in all the
time he'd been held there. He had heard, though, his lawyer, in cahoots
with Marie, had been campaigning tirelessly to secure his release.

Because of this, Frosell had no other choice but to offer the same
defense as the one he'd used the previous half dozen times this
supposed testimony by Delaplace had been leveled at him. "Your
Honor, Monsieur Delaplace was a convicted murderer." Frosell chose
his words carefully. "He was condemned and executed over a year ago,
and I understand there is proof he was coerced into providing a false
testimony." Frosell had managed to piece together the circumstances
around Delaplace's sworn statement: the man had been promised
freedom and money from the handful of his fellow prisoners who had
access to lawyers who knew a little of what was going on. "I believe
the objective of the coercion was nothing more than to silence me
by punishing me as a traitor." Had the whole trial process not been
a complete mockery, the proof of coercion alone would have been
enough to have Frosell released from Fresnes.

The judge seemed in no mood to argue with Frosell—quite possibly
because there really was no real case to answer. Instead, he fixed
Frosell with an icy glare. "Monsieur Frosell, the court has in its
possession *fresh* evidence." He riffled through the stack of papers on
his desk and tried to appear authoritative. "There is another sworn
statement to the effect that you, Oscar Frosell, belonged to the *French
Volunteers against Bolshevism*." The judge paused there, paper in hand,
as if for effect. "This was, as we know, the movement for recruiting
soldiers to fight alongside the Germans on the Russian front."

Frosell groaned. It seemed each time one piece of trumped-up evidence was discredited, yet another arose in its place. "That is absolute and utter nonsense." Frosell truly longed to have his old friend Josef Dzeroginsky by his side; the lawyer was far better at maintaining an even temper than he. "And may I ask who provided this testimony?" His patience was beginning to wear very thin, and for as grim as it was, he found himself wishing he were back in his jail cell.

The judge made a big show of examining the paperwork. "It was signed by Colonel Durvy and passed to the court by the D.G.E.R. I hope you do not intend to try discrediting them too, Monsieur Frosell?"

Of course de Gaulle's Secret Service had to be involved in the production of such a convenient document! Frosell's heart sank as the weight of the new evidence rested upon his shoulders. This was yet another seemingly impossible hurdle for him to face. "Am I correct in assuming Colonel Durvy is to be brought before the court?"

The judge could barely conceal his smile. "Unfortunately, we have been unable to locate the colonel," he informed Frosell with relish. "We have scoured all of France, and he is nowhere to be found."

One of the soldiers stepped forward.

"Yes?" The judge was irritated by the interruption.

"Your Honor," the soldier said. "Colonel Durvy is here."

"Here?"

"At Fresnes. He is a prisoner."

"If that is the case, Your Honor," Frosell grasped at the fragment of hope with both hands, "then he should be summoned."

The judge narrowed his eyes at Frosell and then gave the soldier who had spoken out a particularly hard stare. "Very well. We will adjourn until Colonel Durvy can be brought before the court." He huffed, got to his feet, and stormed out.

It took them four hours to round up the colonel, during which time Frosell rested up the best he could in his tiny cell. At least they'd left the handcuffs off, and he was able to sit on the floor and lean his aching back against the cold stone wall with a modicum of comfort. He was all too aware his time was running out; the French authorities were becoming ever bolder in their fabricated charges and fake testimonies as they attempted to cover up their theft of his property; to Frosell it definitely smacked of little more than sheer desperation. Someday soon they would run out of excuses, and he feared they would likely follow through on their threats of having him executed within the walls of the prison and he would simply "disappear."

When the soldiers came for him, Frosell noted the one who'd spoken up in court was nowhere to be seen. While he was grateful for the soldier revealing Durvy's whereabouts, he couldn't help but feel guilty the man may have landed himself in a lot of trouble for doing so.

Back before the court, Frosell waited patiently as Colonel Durvy, flanked by two soldiers, was escorted in. The man shuffled slowly, hands secured behind his back, his face ashen. As Colonel Durvy peered around the court with terrified eyes, Frosell knew Fresnes had broken him, irreparably so.

"You are Colonel Durvy, former chief of the Anti-Bolshevik Brigade?" The judge's tone was most accusatory and filled with disdain.

"Yes." Durvy kept his eyes downcast, as if the cracked stone floor was of immense interest.

"And you have signed this sworn statement as to Monsieur Frosell's association with your movement?" He waved the paper for emphasis, and Durvy's nod was barely perceptible.

"Would the court care to ascertain under what circumstances the testimony was signed?" Furious, unable to hold his tongue, Frosell was on his feet. Durvy looked up from the floor and stared at Frosell as if he'd seen a ghost.

"Monsieur Frosell!" Anger flashed in the judge's eyes. "Sit down before I have you returned to the cells."

"Monsieur Frosell?" Durvy repeated. "There must be some mistake, Your Honor." Warily, he eyed the judge. "I have never seen this man before in my life."

The judge snorted and glanced at his watch. "But, Monsieur Durvy, you have signed a sworn statement to the effect that Oscar Frosell was a member of your organization."

"May I see the document?" Durvy was quiet and sounded weak. One of the soldiers took the paper from the judge and handed it over to the colonel. "That is *not* my signature, Your Honor," he said with firmness in his trembling voice. "I'm afraid this is nothing more than a poor forgery."

Frosell held his head in his hands. He felt as if he ought to be relieved, as yet another false witness had been debunked and his innocence had once again been proven. He was guilty of nothing more than having German acquaintances, which was something he had not once tried to hide. This entire farce was all about his apartment, his money, and his possessions, and Frosell knew the French would stop at nothing to justify their plundering.

Swedish Consulate, Paris. November 12th, 1947.

Heddy held on tight to her mother's hand as they followed Josef Dzeroginsky through the lobby. This was by no means her first excursion to the huge, intimidating building, but something about the purpose in Mother's step that day had the little girl's heart thumping; even the old lawyer seemed afraid of Marie Frosell, and nothing *ever* scared him!

"I cannot believe the ambassador has refused to meet with us," Marie snapped at Dzeroginsky, as if it was somehow his fault. Heddy watched the poor man recoil. He'd been a reassuring presence since Father had gone away, and although he had seemingly endless patience with Mother's tireless campaigning, Dzeroginsky had visibly aged far more than two years should have shown. "Having to make do with the chargé d'affaires at one's own consulate is simply insulting."

"At least they have agreed to see you this time, Madame Frosell," Dzeroginsky offered. "Maybe they have news for us?" He attempted a smile, but Heddy saw he wasn't in the least bit happy.

"They had *better* have news for us," Marie growled, and Heddy felt her grip tighten around her little fingers. "They have done absolutely nothing in two years; this has all gone on long enough!" She strode with purpose toward the front desk, and Heddy watched as the grim-faced reception lady shrank away from her mother's approach. "We are here to see—"

"Madame Frosell?" The chargé d'affaires stepped forward as if from nowhere. His sudden appearance startled Heddy, who collided with her mother's legs as she stopped dead in her tracks. The little girl stared up at the short, round man with the ruddy face and thinning blond hair and couldn't help but see he appeared to be absolutely terrified of her mother. "I'm Gottfrid Vikander." He spoke slowly and with an almost impenetrably thick accent. He held out his hand to shake Marie's, and then Dzeroginsky's. Heddy was a tad offended the stumpy man in the dark suit ignored her; this was her father they were meeting about, after all!

"If you would like to follow me?" It wasn't a question. Vikander strode off with purpose in the direction of the consulate's many meeting rooms.

Once secured and seated within the confines of the tiny, dour room, Dzeroginsky spoke first. "Will General Consul Raoul Nordling be joining us?" There was a mischievous glint in the lawyer's eye as the chargé d'affaires fiddled nervously with his tie and avoided looking him in the face.

"I'm afraid Monsieur Nordling is tied up with other matters today," Vikander delivered the excuse. "He did say to extend his apologies for not being able to attend the meeting." He then peered down at Heddy, who stood silently by her mother's side.

"Heddy is okay standing, Monsieur Vikander." Marie deflected the man's objection at the child's presence; there was no way she was going to have Heddy removed from the room. "So, do you have any news for us?"

Vikander fiddled with his tie again and studied the small desk that sat between him and his guests. "It transpires the French State Committee of Confiscations actually published their findings in February of last year." He finally summoned the courage to look Marie in the eye. "But, they have yet to make any final decision as to the situation regarding your husband's property—"

"Do you mean to tell us the French have sat on their ruling for twenty-one months?" Dzeroginsky struggled hard to keep his voice down. "That is simply outrageous, monsieur!"

"I agree wholeheartedly, Monsieur Dzeroginsky," Vikander said. "We were only told of this a week ago; I can only apologize."

Marie sat forward in her chair and glowered at the chargé d'affaires. "You must *insist* the French make their final decision," she told him. "My family has waited long enough."

"I'm afraid we are not in a position to—"

"Just do your damn job, will you?" Dzeroginsky's raised voice filled the cramped meeting room. "My client has been incarcerated for over two years while the French procrastinate and construct lies and false testimonies to cover their theft of his property." The lawyer paused for breath and to study Vikander, who appeared to be hopelessly out of his depth. "Once this whole sorry affair goes public, it will not only be General Counsel Nordling who will have to answer for their actions."

The lawyer's thinly veiled threat rested heavy on Vikander. "Attaché Bernstrom has been dealing with the matter," he offered. "I can speak with him to see if he could perhaps lobby the French for a final decision?"

"I'm appalled this has not been done already." Marie steadied her voice; she was determined not to play the weak, emotional little wife in front of Vikander. "What has the consulate been doing all this time to secure my husband's release?"

Vikander didn't appear to have an answer for her.

"I think we should *all* speak with Attaché Bernstrom," Dzeroginsky insisted. "Since we are all here today, I'm sure that will be convenient, Monsieur Vikander?"

With a heavy sigh, the chargé d'affaires stood up from his chair. "If you would like to wait here, I'm sure I can find him." He appeared relieved at having the matter pushed onto someone else.

"We have all day; we can wait," Dzeroginsky told him. "So may I suggest you fetch Bernstrom and we bring this sorry affair to its conclusion before my client spends any more unnecessary time in prison?"

Suitably chastised, Vikander shuffled from the meeting room and was pleased to be away from the aggressive lawyer and his client's wife and eerily silent daughter.

CHAPTER TWENTY-ONE

Fresnes Jail, Fresnes, Val-de-Marne. November 27th, 1947.

Following his customary five a.m. wake-up call by the snarling soldiers and their machine guns, Frosell was once more bundled into the Black Maria, transported the short distance to the prison's courtroom, and shoved into the underground holding cell, which had almost become like a second home during his stay at Fresnes.

At around noon, as the soldiers came to escort him to the court, Frosell resigned himself to yet another farce; he couldn't help but wonder what fabricated "evidence" and false testimonies the French had in store for him this time. Despite feeling weary down to his chilled bones, Frosell walked into the makeshift courtroom with his head held high. For as much as they'd worn him down, he was determined they wouldn't see how weak he'd become over the course of the two years and some he'd spend in that God-awful jail.

Frosell's resolve all but crumbled when he saw Marie at the rear of the court. Wearing a dark gray skirt suit and flanked by a pair of gun-toting soldiers, his wife stood next to Josef Dzeroginsky, who looked most officious. A little way in front of them stood a man

Frosell didn't recognize. Frosell smiled at Marie, and he saw that she, too, had tears in her eyes.

This was the first time the court had allowed Frosell any form of representation, let alone his wife. This was the first time he'd laid eyes on Marie since his incarceration at Fresnes, and her presence in the preposterous farce of a court lifted his spirits a thousandfold.

The judge took his seat and insisted Frosell remain standing. "This won't take long, Monsieur Frosell," he grunted. "We are only here to inform you of the findings of the State Committee of Confiscations."

Frosell's heart lifted.

At last! After two hellish years, on top of the months of persecution preceding them, the French had come to their senses and finally realized that justice *had* to be served.

"The court recognizes the accused's legal counsel, and Attaché Knut J.R. Bernstrom of the Swedish Legation." He gave a cursory nod in their general direction.

Frosell found it amusing the judge—who, in keeping with all of the fake court judges to date, hadn't given his name—was going to such great pains to be official and do everything by the book simply because the attaché was in attendance; such formalities, to date, had been willfully neglected.

The judge shuffled through a thin collection of paperwork on his desk. He cleared his throat and spoke slowly, as if Frosell were a simpleton. "It is the finding of the State Committee of Confiscations that Oscar Frosell is guilty of illegal profiteering during the war, and as such will pay two hundred and fifty million francs to the state."

Frosell struggled to believe the words the judge had just delivered; surely he had misheard? He barely registered his wife's shocked gasp from the rear of the courtroom or his lawyer's footsteps as Dzeroginsky made his way to the bench.

"Furthermore, Monsieur Frosell," the judge continued, "you are hereby sentenced to four years in prison, the confiscation of all present and future possessions, a fine of one hundred thousand francs, costs of one hundred and thirty thousand francs, and for a period of twenty years, the loss of your rights as a French subject."

Stunned into silence, Frosell stood before the judge and struggled to comprehend what he was hearing: had the French State finally sanctioned the pillaging of his home and property? And it intended to punish him for alleged crimes, which had absolutely no foundation? Surely not!

"We would appreciate a copy of the official judgment, Your Honor." Dzeroginsky stepped forward and took his place by Frosell's side. "It must be held up to scrutiny."

The judge glanced across the room at Attaché Bernstrom. "The court has the *summary* of the judgment." He lifted up a handful of papers. "You will have to request a copy of the full, official judgment from the Swedish Embassy."

The lawyer snorted and lifted his eyes to the ceiling as if in silent prayer; he knew full well there'd be no official judgment, and thus the legality of the court's sentence upon his client had to be held up to question. He also knew any appeal was likely to take many months, years perhaps, and all the while, Frosell was to be held in prison and would most likely die there.

Continuing, the judge informed Frosell, "You are to be immediately taken from here and transported to Oermigen prison camp. You will serve out the entirety of your sentence there."

"No!" Marie cried out and ran to her husband; even the soldiers hadn't the heart to stop her.

Frosell held his wife tight as they said their goodbyes. He told her to take good care of Heddy and he'd be home before they knew it; Dzeroginsky would lodge an appeal with the French courts that very afternoon.

"Take him away." The judge was impatient, as if he had far more important things to attend to. He got to his feet and, as the soldiers removed Oscar Frosell from his wife's arms, he made his way out of the courtroom and slipped out through a side door.

CHAPTER TWENTY-TWO

Oermigen Concentration Camp. April 18ᵗʰ, 1948.

As Oscar Frosell made peace and prepared himself for death, the soldier let out a loud, jovial laugh that sounded so cold and heartless in the damp, cold courtyard. Frosell glanced across at the soldier, wary and confused because of the gun pointed at his head, although he noticed the soldier's finger was no longer on the trigger.

"It would seem it is your lucky night, *collaborateur*." The other soldier stepped the short way across the courtyard. He swung his gun limply from one hand and appeared to be having trouble walking in a straight line. "It looks like your Nazi friends haven't forgotten you after all." He knocked his colleague's gun away from Frosell's temple. "Put that away," he barked. "We have to take him out of here."

Frosell's erstwhile executioner gave his comrade a puzzled look as he uncocked and holstered his Luger. "Back to his cell? I thought we were to dispose of him?"

"No, stupid," spat the drunken soldier. "We *are* disposing of him." He held up a hand and rubbed forefinger and thumb together. "The *Gestapo* has been bailed."

Frosell studied the young soldier as the message finally got through to his wine-soaked brain. His own mind spun. He was still reeling from the almost execution, which he'd expected was going to come sooner rather than later from the moment he'd been sentenced to Oermigen. He was little more than an embarrassment to the French now that they had completely—illegally—justified their actions, so it was only a matter of time before they made him disappear completely. As to how he was to be sprung from the jail—that much remained a mystery.

The soldiers dragged Frosell from the courtyard and marched him along the dark hallways in the opposite direction to the cell—his home for six months.

As the ominous shape of the camp's front door loomed ahead, Frosell's chest tightened; it was still entirely possible this was the last step of removing him—permanently.

The drunken soldier opened the prison door just enough for Frosell to slip through and see a long, black car moving at a snail's pace on the road beyond. "Au revoir, *collaborateur*." He shoved Frosell hard in the back, which sent him sprawling out on the walkway outside. He fell hard, the breath knocked from his weakened body, and by the time he looked back, the door was closed and the guards gone.

The black car loomed ever closer.

Frosell picked himself up off the ground. Panicked, he looked around; of course, no one was out at such a late hour, and the lights in the prison's guard room, which normally blazed night and day, had been switched off.

Should he run? Frosell doubted he had the energy to get far if he did. He'd cheated death once that night, and he didn't think he could summon the energy to do so again. But, as the car drew up beside him, Frosell knew he at least had to try—this was his first taste of freedom in so long, he owed it to Marie and Heddy to make the most of it.

Frosell turned to run.

"Oscar!" Marie's voice froze him to the spot.

"You must get into the car, monsieur." He recognized Dzeroginsky's gruff tone and spun around.

"Josef?" Frosell stared through the car's open door at his wife, Heddy, and Dzeroginsky; he also cast a glance at the short blond man who occupied the driver's seat.

"He's a friend." Dzeroginsky pointed at the driver as Frosell clambered into the car. Heddy stirred as Frosell and Marie hugged and she murmured, "Hello, Father" as if she were dreaming. "I'm afraid we didn't have the luxury of time to appeal the decision; you were to be eliminated tonight," the lawyer explained as he pulled the car's door closed and the vehicle sped away from the prison. "This really was the only way."

"Who did you bribe, Josef?"

"The right people, Oscar; that's all you need to know." Dzeroginsky offered nothing more, and Frosell knew it would be prudent not to press him; as a lawyer, the man was most adept at evading awkward questions when he needed to.

Marie held onto her husband. She had grown to believe, following his sentencing at Fresnes, she would never see him alive again; she'd even gone so far as to begin preparing Heddy for the worst, especially after seeing his poor state of health in court.

"Where are we going, Josef?" Frosell turned to his lawyer.

"I'm going home, Oscar," Dzeroginsky told him. "I have appeals to lodge in Paris; I'm right in thinking you're still wanting me to do that?"

"Of course," Frosell told him. "But surely we can't return to Saint-Cloud as if nothing has happened."

The lawyer shook his head. "I have arranged for you to leave the country, Oscar," he said. "I have a little money for your journey, and the embassy has arranged for you to be granted asylum and to provide temporary accommodation."

Frosell fixed Dzeroginsky with a steely gaze. "Where are we going, Josef?"

The lawyer offered Frosell a pained smile, which was meant to be reassuring. "It's the best we could do under the circumstances, Oscar. You're going home—to Stockholm, to be exact." Of course, Dzeroginsky knew his client had never set foot in Sweden. Born in Canada, raised in Greece, and schooled in England, Frosell had attended university in Heidelberg and traveled to Germany and Italy before settling in France; Oscar Frosell would be a stranger in his home country. Even so, being a Swedish citizen, there really had been no other option for Dzeroginsky—the priority was to get his client out of the country before the French disposed of him completely. With a heavy heart, the lawyer fished out an envelope of money, an unopened packet of cigarettes, and a lighter. He handed them over to Frosell and endured the remainder of the journey to Paris in silence.

And so, with little more than the clothes on their backs, Oscar Frosell, Marie, and Heddy fled France under the cover of night.

CHAPTER TWENTY-THREE

Stockholm. June 1951.

"You promised to take Heddy to Skansen Zoo today, Oscar," Marie chastised her husband. "The weather's perfect for it." She peeped through the shabby curtain at the blue, cloudless skies that reminded her so much of the happier times at Cosne-Cours-sur-Loire.

Heddy watched with expectation as her father huffed and refused to take his eyes off the fat pile of haphazardly stacked papers occupying the area of the small sofa he did not. In fact, there were papers absolutely *everywhere* she cared to look in their tiny apartment; Father had taken the place over as surely as his obsession had absorbed him.

Monsieur Dzeroginsky had sent many of the papers over from Paris; although he was no longer the family's lawyer, he maintained a sincere interest in the case and had recommended an excellent lawyer in Stockholm. Other heaps of papers were Father's endless research notes and typed-up pages for the book he was determined to write about his injustice at the hands of the French. He'd tap it all out, night and day, on a rickety old typewriter balanced on a small, ancient table—both of which he'd bought for a few krona at a local junk store.

The two small rooms in the occupied apartment the Swedish welfare had arranged upon the family's furtive arrival in the country had been cramped, to say the least. It was owned by an old, grumpy widower who lived alone and never seemed to have so much as a smile or a kind word for anyone. He had rented out what used to be the servants quarters a long time ago—an old, dark apartment with small windows along one side of a long hallway, which led to an equally antiquated kitchen. A small refrigerator was available for their use, but Marie was allocated only one shelf in it. Marie had been allowed one hour per day in the kitchen to prepare a meal for her family.

The Frosells had a bedroom in which all three slept, with Heddy on a small, foldable cot. The remainder of the apartment consisted of a small, windowless, terribly cluttered room with only a table and three chairs; and a small toilet and matching sink. For three long years they lived there—a far cry from the sumptuous Rue Dufrenoy apartment they'd so loved.

At that time, in the austere years of post-war Europe, welfare was not as generous as it would become in later, more prosperous years, and the money Oscar and his family were given for food was barely enough to cover even their most basic needs, let alone enough for a decent meal. In order to make ends meet and feed her husband and growing daughter, Marie would often resort to asking nearby grocery stores for leftover bread; old, often sprouting potatoes; and cabbage from which she managed to make delicious soups.

The money Frosell had taken from the safe on the day they'd fled Rue Dufrenoy at the behest of Admiral Dumesnil was long gone, as was the jewelry Marie had grabbed before leaving; it had all been spent on rent, food, and living expenses, as well as lawyers and bribes back in Paris. Frosell had thankfully managed to find lawyers in Stockholm willing to work *pro bono* on the promise of a slice of the family fortune once justice was done and restitution made, otherwise suing the Swedish government would have been completely out of the question.

For as much as the family's hardships broke her heart, Marie wouldn't allow Heddy to complain; even though the little girl only had two changes of clothes—both donated by welfare—she impressed upon her to be grateful they had a roof over their heads and her father was no longer in prison.

At least the new rented studio apartment, made affordable by Marie's administrative job with a local insurance company, was all theirs and was a tad more spacious. It was still only one room, had no bedroom—only a compact sofa bed that Oscar would pull down every evening—and what passed as the kitchen comprised nothing more than a single heating plate in the corner of the room. But, given all that, the family didn't have to share it with anyone, which was a luxury all in itself.

With the family having a little income coming in, Marie was able to make a meatloaf, which was 50/50 bread and cheap minced meat, and the family had to make it last for the duration of the week. Still, they had no extra money to afford desserts, sweets, or candies, and not enough to celebrate birthdays, Christmas, or any of the other holidays either that Heddy had once looked forward to with eager anticipation.

Heddy was too ashamed to tell anyone at school where she lived, or about her new, frugal life; she was bullied enough as it was—for being a poor welfare child *and* a foreigner—and due to the sheltered life she lived, she found it increasingly difficult to make friends.

"I can't bring her to the zoo," Frosell grumped. "I have a meeting at one with Larsson; we are to discuss the progress of his application to the Swedish Foreign Office." Dag Larsson was Frosell's new lawyer; he'd picked up where Dzeroginsky had left off. "He's spoken to Gunnar Fant, who agreed to write a report to the Board of Guardians on Heddy's behalf." The lawyer's personal friendship with Fant, a former mayor of Stockholm, had proven particularly useful in pushing Frosell's case forward; in fact, it had been the primary decider in Dzeroginsky's recommendation of the man. "Under French law, they are not allowed to confiscate any property belonging to you or Heddy. That means at least half of what they took, they took illegally—even if their fabricated charges were to be real." He lit up another cigarette and took a long, deep drag.

"But Heddy is missing out on so much, Oscar," Marie protested. "It's only a trip to the zoo . . ."

"The girl can go to the damn zoo as often as she wants when we get restitution." Frosell's rote reply was met with a heavy-hearted sigh.

"We can't keep putting off Heddy's childhood, my love." Marie struggled to keep her emotions in check; watching her dear husband become so completely consumed by his obsession had become as difficult to bear as having him in prison. "It could take years, and once Heddy is grown, we won't be able to get these years back—no matter how much compensation you are awarded from the French government."

"Larsson requested the foreign office make a demarche and to supply the money for Dzeroginsky to look after our legal rights in Paris." Frosell seemed to not have heard a word his wife had said. He sucked on his cigarette until the red ember at its end touched the cheap Bakelite holder he'd bought to replace his broken one. "They turned the request down."

Marie touched his arm. "I'm so sorry, my love—"

"The minister of foreign affairs actually stated he believes our case is best kept a secret." Frosell harrumphed and fought to control his temper; his disdain for Osten Unden was practically palpable. "In the interests of the *third man*—can you believe the audacity of it?"

Heddy picked up her notepad and retreated to a corner of the room—there'd be no zoo today, that much was obvious—and she began to draw and write another of the fantastical tales to take her away from the cramped apartment and her ever-obsessed father.

Although Heddy was bitterly disappointed—she'd been looking forward to a trip to the zoo—she was far too intimidated by her father to say anything. He was not a man one ever spoke up against; she had witnessed that in his dealings with all manner of people, no matter what their level of authority, and the truth was that she barely knew him. He'd been in jail throughout much of her formative years, when a little girl would build a relationship with her father that would last her entire life and imprint on her psyche the model for her future husband. And, upon his release and the family's escape to Sweden, Frosell was far too busy fighting the French for retribution to have any time for Heddy or her poor mother, Marie; it was a 24/7 job for him, and little else mattered. In effect, life had stopped for Frosell the moment he fled the prison and France, and he seemed unable to grasp how come it couldn't stop for Heddy too. He seemed to fully expect time to stand still until he'd won his case against the French and Swedish governments and the family's fortune had been restored.

Of course, Marie's pleas for her dear husband to take a break from what he considered his work to pay some attention to their growing daughter fell on deaf ears; all he would say was there would be plenty of time for such niceties and to do what a child-cum-teenager ought to be doing.

Precisely due to this state of affairs, Heddy had no friends at all, no socialization outside of school, and she craved to be in her parents' company all the time. Her circumstances also ensured the development of the little girl's vivid imagination as she learned how to entertain herself and be comfortable with only her own company; she would write and illustrate her own fairy tales for years to come.

"Of course, His *Excellency* means Raoul Nordling," Frosell continued, "who is being lauded as a national hero in France, along with his co-conspirator, the president; anyone would think it was de

Gaulle who'd won the damn war!" Nordling's initial insistence that Frosell was not a Swedish citizen still hung heavy over the family; had the general consul been truthful about Frosell's nationality from the beginning, then most of the family's fortune would likely still be intact. And, while exposing Nordling as a self-serving liar was not his top priority for gaining restitution, it was certainly high up on Oscar Frosell's list.

"It's just so typical of the Swedish government," Frosell said through a thick cloud of cigarette smoke. "Unden did exactly the same with the Raoul Wallenberg affair—a diplomat is kidnapped by the Russians, and he went to extraordinary lengths to hush it all up. It's one thing being a neutral country, but entirely another to be too frightened to speak up for your citizens." He lit another cigarette from the glowing stump of the old one and slotted it into the holder. "The Swiss managed to protect their citizens from wartime plundering and have obtained compensation where sentences were carried out. I firmly believe, had we been Swiss, we'd still be living in Paris."

Marie had heard it all before, of course. It had been incredibly difficult for her to live with the man she loved, as he spent every waking minute on his research, legal papers, and the confounded book; his only topics of conversation were the French, the Dumesnils, de Gaulle, and, of course, Raoul Nordling. He'd steadfastly refused to work, which meant providing for the family had become Marie's sole responsibility, and he had become increasingly isolated from both her and Heddy. The girl was growing fast and needed a father in her life, and yet all he did was fob her off. Marie was concerned that Heddy—a bright, intelligent, highly imaginative child—was becoming ever more introspective as a result of her father's neglect.

Naturally, the near-constant death and kidnap threats against Heddy only served to add to Marie's stress. They would come via Dzeroginsky in Paris, via Larsson, and sometimes directly from France; her husband swore the threats were from the Dumesnils, or even de Gaulle himself, but offered little in the way of evidence to support such outlandish theories.

And, as much as Marie tried to protect Heddy from the worry of it all, she'd had no option but to instill some level of paranoia in the girl, albeit for the purposes of self-preservation. Heddy had it drilled into her by her parents that she must always be vigilant, trust no one, and never, *ever* go with anyone but her father or mother.

Marie walked Heddy the mile to and from school each day before work, which made her daughter the only eleven-year-old to be accompanied by her mother; of course, it did nothing to alleviate the relentless bullying the poor girl endured day in, day out. It had become a necessary evil, though, following the incident in which the principal had interrupted class to ask Heddy to go with her, as there were some people who wished to speak with her.

Panicking, her parents' stern words firing warnings off in her head, Heddy had instead run by the principal, out of the school, and all the way home.

Father had been furious, of course. And, while Heddy had not been party to her father's angry dressing-down of the principal, she knew her behavior had been serious enough for her never to return to the school again.

After that incident, Oscar and Marie insisted their daughter accompany them absolutely everywhere they went; she was not allowed out of their sight anywhere out of the family apartment. Those were trying times for the young girl, especially so because her parents were adamant she adhere to their "a child must be seen and not heard" policy at all times. As a consequence, much of Heddy's formative years were spent sitting stock-still and silent in a seemingly endless procession of hard, wooden chairs while her mother and father had their many, many conferences and consultations with lawyers and officials about their case against the French government.

At those times, Heddy's imagination kicked in to save her sanity; the little girl would drift off into the wonderful worlds she created for herself and make up increasingly elaborate stories to keep her highly active mind entertained. And, over the years, Heddy did get something out of those childhood experiences: she learned she would never need another person for company, nor did she ever feel lonely.

Frosell pushed the small table back and, clamping the cigarette holder firmly between pursed lips, he got to his feet. "You know how important this is to me." He took hold of Marie's hand. "This is about much more than the money, you have to understand that." He glanced around at the unruly heaps of paperwork dominating the diminutive apartment and a wry smile played upon his lips. "This is about you and Heddy. The French have not only stolen her inheritance, they've taken away her future; do you think I want to raise our daughter in a place like this?"

Marie gave her husband's hand a squeeze. He was a proud, stubborn man who had allowed his obsession to dominate every aspect of his life and to use Heddy as the justification. There was no doubt at all in her mind that, had Oscar taken advantage of his wealth of business contacts and applied his exceptional entrepreneurial skills, he'd have been back on his feet in no time at all. Instead, he spent his days poring over legal documents, witness statements, and his own writings while she went out to work to put food on the table, and Heddy missed out on having a real family. Still, it wasn't in Marie's nature to complain or criticize; she simply went about the business of keeping her small family together in the hope Oscar would gain the recompense he was due and life would become considerably better for all three of them.

Of course, Heddy grew up knowing what her dear father was capable of, and she couldn't help but pick up on her mother's personal disquiet; even from a young age living in that grim, cramped apartment, Heddy would question—silently, of course—why the great and versatile businessman, Oscar Frosell, didn't simply reapply his talents to something else so it didn't fall upon Mother's shoulders to support the entire family. Also at that time, Heddy vowed to herself she would someday give her dear, sweet, ever-patient mother back at least some of the life she had given up in support of her husband's quest for restitution.

"I'll try to be back before dinner," Frosell told his wife. He looked across at Heddy, who was alternating her time between scribbling in her notebook and playing with paper dolls. "But you know how Larsson loves to talk." He laughed a little as he pulled on his jacket and plucked his cigarettes from where they nestled next to his typewriter. "He says he has news for me about the start date for the trial, and I have a feeling it's going to be *good* news." Frosell made his way out of the apartment door, his head all but concealed by a cloud of smoke. "I'm confident we'll be in court and have this whole sorry mess sorted out before Christmas." Closing the door gently behind him, and with a spring in his step, Oscar Frosell went on his way.

CHAPTER TWENTY-FOUR

The Supreme Court of Sweden, Stockholm. February 1959.

Heddy had turned twenty only the month before, and her childhood was well and truly behind her. She sat by her father's side—along with her mother, Dag Larsson, and Josef Dzeroginsky, who had traveled all the way from Paris especially for the occasion—as they awaited with growing optimism the court's verdict only he, it seemed, had believed possible.

For eight long years, Heddy had taken a back seat while her father fought legal battle after legal battle with the French and the Swedish Foreign Office. Frosell had spent more time over those years with Dag Larsson than he'd had quality time with his family. His obsession for restitution had continued to consume him, and now it was all that remained of the Oscar Frosell his daughter and long-suffering wife had once known and loved.

Frosell had involved his daughter in his fight the moment she'd mastered the Swedish language, even though he'd learned it quickly himself once they were safely ensconced in Stockholm way back in 1948. Even so, Frosell decided to use Heddy as his translator between his lawyer and the courts; he'd become so immersed in the minutiae of the legalities, he'd failed to see it was no life for a growing teenaged girl. Heddy had little choice but to comply, even though her father was a ruthless taskmaster. He refused to accept any mistakes or hesitation, even from a child, and a large part of the compliance was simply because he struck such an imposing character that she actually feared him.

Thankfully, Heddy was a fast learner and quickly familiarized herself with all the official terms and titles of government and the legal system; by the time she left school at age sixteen, Heddy was incredibly proficient at translating—without hesitation—everything that was said while it was spoken.

Immediately after quitting school, Heddy worked alongside her mother at the insurance company, having taken full advantage of the state-offered free schooling to train in bookkeeping and secretarial work. And, with the both of them earning—for the entirety of those eight years, her father had eschewed work in favor of his legal battles—they were able to afford a modest apartment on the outskirts of Stockholm. The place was small, but at least it was bigger than their previous accommodations, it had more than one room, and was a short subway ride into the city.

The courtroom was awash with whispered conversations, and the air of anticipation among the sparse collection of court officials, lawyers, and casual observers as they awaited the judge was all but tangible; the verdict was almost fifteen years in the making and had cost Oscar Frosell his health, his family, and his daughter's formative years.

"All rise." The clerk of the court's voice echoed about the high ceiling and brought a reverent hush to the room.

Frosell and his entourage rose as instructed and watched as the judge made his way in and took his seat.

"Good luck, Oscar," Dzeroginsky whispered.

Frosell smiled. "There is no luck about this, Josef," he told the lawyer. "Our case is absolutely watertight—there can only be one verdict."

"Oscar Frosell," the judge read from the docket before him, "it is the finding of this court that the decision of the Confiscation Committee that you were to pay two hundred and fifty million francs without any existing motive and with false official information, hearsay, and unwarranted assumptions are of no legal value and are in contradiction of the laws and rulings of all civilized countries."

Frosell's heart raced. Finally, his own government was acknowledging the wrongs of the French state.

"Furthermore, the total sum of the property, goods, and chattels illegally seized by judgment of the Seine Special Court of Justice—for which you were granted amnesty—is calculated at one billion francs."

The judge's words hung heavy in the air. Of course, Frosell knew the full worth of his possessions—the stamp collection was worth two hundred and fifty million francs alone—but hearing it spoken out loud sent chills along his spine; the sheer magnitude of France's pillaging was staggering.

The judge explained to the silent court how, since Sweden was a neutral state, Frosell was perfectly entitled to trade in France with German troops, in accordance with the legitimate government at the time, which meant that such dealings were started by Pétain's government and were therefore entirely lawful, even if the Swedish Foreign Office decreed he had worked with the occupying forces, which he had not.

It all became just so many words to Frosell. He had lived and breathed every minute detail of the accusations thrown at him, the state-sanctioned pillaging of his property, and not to mention the illegal incarceration and near execution. Having his arguments affirmed by the Swedish court was like a dream come true; finally, he was going to get the restitution he and his family so richly deserved.

"The court is satisfied that Oscar Frosell did not engage in trade or trafficking with anyone, and have found no evidence to the contrary." The judge paused for a sip of tepid water. "The official looting of private property and official embezzlement of private belongings of the Frosell family cannot be justified by retrospective charges and ulterior convictions; this is in complete contradiction with the basic and fundamental principles of human rights and international law."

Frosell shot a smile at Marie, who in turn reached for his hand. This was it—they had finally won! All the years of doubting her husband's conviction and her own lack of faith in the legal system had proved her wrong; perhaps now she would get her husband back.

The judge appeared keen to wrap up, as if the judgment he was delivering weighed too heavily on his shoulders. "Moreover, any requisition of whatever nature is entitled to compensation and must be indemnified in full; otherwise it legally loses its requisition value and becomes nothing more than official pillaging."

Throughout the judgment, General Consul Raoul Nordling's name was conspicuous by its absence; not even the Swedish High Court deemed it necessary to drag the name of the man who saved Paris through the legal mud. Frosell would have preferred to see the man's duplicitous actions held up for all to see, but figured he'd have to be happy with full restitution of his family's fortune, at least for now. The trial had lasted from February 1951 to February 1959.

It was over.

Finally.

All the years of running like common criminals, of having everything they owned taken away, living like paupers, the lost time Frosell had spent in prison; it had all come to a glorious end. The family's wealth was to be restored—by the French—and Heddy's future would be assured. While Frosell's obsession had driven him to fight every single step of the way, there was a big part of it he'd done for his daughter.

And, while Nordling, Admiral Dumesnil and his heinous wife and daughter, and even de Gaulle himself remained untainted by the deplorable way in which the family had been treated, Frosell was determined he would tell his story to the world and expose them for the despicable human beings they truly were.

The judge had barely finished delivering his judgment when a cheer rang out in the courtroom. Frosell hugged Marie and Heddy and gave the two lawyers a hearty handshake.

"We did it, Marie." Frosell's face, gaunt and pale from so many years of stress, managed a broad smile as he held his family for what felt to be the first time since they'd left Paris to embark upon their ordeal.

Oscar Frosell left the court a changed man. Naturally, his obsession was so deep-rooted he was already planning how best to let the world know who exactly had been responsible for such an appalling travesty of justice, and to let the Swedish people know their government was far too preoccupied with covering up injustices meted out on its citizens than taking care of their interests. Even having won restitution, Frosell's fight was far from over.

He, Marie, and Heddy had a celebratory dinner with Dzeroginsky and Larsson. It was accompanied by the obligatory amounts of the best champagne, before the Frosells said their goodbyes to the lawyers and made their way home in the cool evening air. It was all such a far cry from the opulence of 6 Rue Dufrenoy, but they finally had realistic hope of being able to look forward to living a normal life, if not in luxury.

EPILOGUE

Oscar Frosell died of a brain tumor in 1965.

Sadly, and despite the legal judgment of the Swedish courts, the Frosells received not one penny in restitution. Both the French and Swedish governments acknowledged the illegal plundering of the family's property, but neither considered themselves liable for the compensation—even the proportion rightfully belonging to Marie and Heddy.

To this day, the whereabouts of the Frosells' art, furniture, and stamp collections remain unknown.

Frosell spent the remaining years of his life writing a book that would never be published, and fighting for the recompense he had given so much of his life to win; he died a broken man.

Raoul Nordling died in 1961 and was written in the history books as the man who did, indeed, save Paris from the Nazis. As he had dreamed, a movie was made of the historical event; Andre Dussollier portrayed him as a great hero of the Second World War.

Admiral Charles-Henri Dumesnil died in Paris, in 1946; his prowess as a naval commander remains legendary.

Alla Dumesnil died in Paris, in 1999. She was heralded as a war hero and savior of France.

Charles de Gaulle remained in office until 1969, and died, at age seventy-nine, in 1970.

Following her father's death, Heddy took great care of Marie. She vowed to give her the life she had missed out on because of Oscar's fixation and imprisonment. Marie Frosell died in 2011.

Heddy Frosell made her own way, without the family's fortune, as an air hostess in the early days of commercial flight. She lives to this day in the United States of America.

END

AUTHOR'S FOOTNOTE

Throughout my life, I have always felt guilty I couldn't do something with the four thick books my father spent his life writing about every detail of our family's ordeal at the hands of the French and Swedish governments.

For many, many decades I thought my only choice would be to get myself a lawyer and start all over again, and to sue those governments for at least the portion of the family money that legally belonged to my mother and me.

However, I was realistic enough to know it would never result in justice for us, since no government so readily accepts any wrongdoing, especially that done during wartime. And, almost all of those involved are long dead by now, and I don't have the thousands of dollars it would take to bring such a case to trial.

So, as I started on my bucket list, I thought how sad it would be to let my family's story die with me and never be told.

It does seem to me there is an interest in real-life stories lately, so I figured that at least a book was in order . . .

Heddy Frosell da Ponte
October 2019